Thomas M Bewley

February 1952

THE STORY OF ST. LUKE'S HOSPITAL

[Frontispiece

Major-General the Rt. Hon. The Earl of Athlone,
K.G., G.C.B., G.C.M.G., G.C.V.O., D.S.O.

president, st. luke's hospital, 1931-1948.

The Story of St. Luke's Hospital

by

BRIGADIER C. N. FRENCH, C.M.G., C.B.E.

With a Foreword by

Sir GEORGE COCKERILL, C.B.

LONDON

WILLIAM HEINEMANN ◆ MEDICAL BOOKS ◆ LTD

1951

First Published 1951

Dedicated
by permission
to
Major-General the Right Hon. The Earl of Athlone,
K.G., P.C., G.C.B., G.C.M.G., G.C.V.O., D.S.O.

*This book is copyright. It may not be
reproduced in whole or in part, nor may
illustrations be copied for any purpose,
without permission. Application with
regard to copyright should be addressed
to the Publishers.*

PRINTED IN GREAT BRITAIN BY
THE CHISWICK PRESS, NEW SOUTHGATE, N.11

CONTENTS

ILLUSTRATIONS

FOREWORD

THE question has been posed, in connection with the work of a very eminent writer, "whether literary introductions are any conceivable use", or, in other words, "whether there is any earthly reason why anyone should introduce anyone else's work". I do not know the appropriate answer to the general question but to the particular question whether any real reason exists, earthly or otherwise, why I should write a foreword to Brigadier Charles French's admirable "Story of St. Luke's Hospital" there can be but one response—that there is none. The ostensible reason for my enjoying this privilege is the fact that I was a Governor of St. Luke's Hospital during the whole period that Brigadier French filled the position of Secretary and am therefore perhaps qualified to appraise the value of his devoted services during those critical years. Not the least of these services I suggest has been the labour involved in compiling this most interesting story of the Hospital's foundation and subsequent history.

This book is the fruit of the author's meticulous search through the minutes of the Court and of the General and House Committees and such other records as the Hospital possesses. These latter unfortunately were found to be less complete than could have been wished. Receipts were available for only a limited number of years and the same could be said of letters and similar documents. It is indeed a remarkable tribute to the author's industry and pertinacity that he has succeeded in extracting from such scanty records so complete a story of the Hospital. It might seem that every Hospital and similar Institution should keep not only minutes but also such other records as would be useful in compiling its history: certainly in the case of St. Luke's Hospital the existence of fuller records would have greatly reduced the labours of its historian.

One fact clearly emerges. The Hospital owed its inception over 200 years ago to the humanitarian feelings of six City gentlemen "moved to pity", as Brigadier French observes, "for their suffering fellow-citizens. It did not derive from any monastic foundation nor from any single benefactor but from

... plain well-to-do City merchants". From the first it was supported solely by voluntary contributions from others of the same mind and of the same class; it was in fact a typical example of individual effort and private enterprise leading the advance to better things. The founders were just plain citizens unconnected with the Government either of the country or of its chief city, though certainly well informed of the daily lives and real needs of the people. There were no rich endowments and no subsidies. The funds of the Hospital were laboriously accumulated out of gifts from humane persons and contributions from the charitable public. There was consequently never a time when the Governors were relieved of the necessity of jealously husbanding their resources. The best evidence of their success is to be found in the fact that they not only maintained but increased their general fund as time went on, and, on amalgamation with the Middlesex Hospital, contributed a modern and well-equipped Hospital. Its evolution during a period of 200 years from a Hospital for poor lunatics to the St. Luke's–Woodside Branch of the Middlesex Hospital is traced with great skill in the following pages, from which, I cannot but think, many lessons of great value to the community can readily be drawn.

London, 1951   GEORGE COCKERILL

THE FOUNDING OF ST. LUKE'S AND THE FIRST HOSPITAL

THE history of lunacy is too large a subject to touch on here more than briefly and superficially, but some account of the care and treatment, such as they were, of the mentally afflicted before the middle of the eighteenth century is desirable in order to appreciate the progress made and to some extent influenced by the charity of St. Luke's during its existence as a City Hospital.

The treatment of the insane in England during the Middle Ages and down to the beginning of the nineteenth century reflects little credit on medical knowledge or the imagination of the public generally. During these centuries the people of England were then, as now, fighters to a man—generally barbarous in their sports, rough, insensitive and often cruel, but though they were tough they were not sadists, indeed fundamentally and in many essentials they were kindly folk. To them, however, the lunatic was not "the afflicted of God" but on the contrary one possessed by an evil spirit. Hence the constant use of the whip both within those few hospitals where the insane were received and their cure attempted, and also outside those institutions. Hence also the practice of dragging afflicted persons, bound with ropes or manacled with chains and collars of iron, to the foot of the altar where they were left for the night in the hope that the morning might see them worn out physically but restored mentally.

Those who were free to wander where they would on the highways were often cruelly beaten—"whipped from tything to tything"—as described by Edgar in *King Lear*, or ducked in the nearest pond until from sheer exhaustion they had no fighting or violent spirit left in them. Nevertheless, the open road, despite the chance, or rather the probability, of such treatment, was probably preferable to some form of cure with chains and an iron collar and in addition some form of terrorism which would have been their portion had they fallen into the hands of the medical profession or the justices of those days.

Even as late as 1807 it was said that there was hardly a parish in which might not be found some unfortunate creature, chained in the cellar or garret of a workhouse, perhaps shut up in an uninhabited ruin, or rambling half-naked and starved through the streets or highways, laughed at and mocked by the vulgar and ignorant.

Bethlem Hospital was to a certain extent an exception, but, in the main, its treatment of patients reflected the views and ignorance of contemporary physicians. This house was founded as a Priory in 1247, and it is recorded as early as 1377 that insane persons were housed there. It may be assumed that before the Reformation all the attendants were at least nominally clergy, but that did not prevent them from taking fraudulent advantage of their position to rob the hospital and starve the patients.

After the Reformation, Henry VIII granted (at a price), the control and government of St. Bartholomew's and Bethlem Hospitals to the Lord Mayor and Corporation of London, but the condition of the lunatics in the latter hospital was not improved under municipal management. Eventually as a result of complaints that had reached him, James I sent Commissioners to enquire into the treatment of the patients by the then Keeper, and the King, whose precepts were generally better than his practice, reminded them before their enquiry that those who suffered from mental affliction ought to be "treated with all the care necessary by the rules of medicine". Further he ordered them to dismiss any of those in charge who were without skill and to do what they could to raise the hospital to the level of St. Bartholomew's and St. Thomas's.

This enquiry produced some improvement in the treatment of lunatics, but there was for many years a suspicion that the keepers stole the patients' food, accepted bribes and added to their perquisites in whatever way they could.

It should be remembered, however, that the standard of honesty down to the end of the eighteenth century was not high in any walk of life. Sir Robert Walpole did not invent the system of corruption but took advantage of and improved it for his political ends. Moreover, although money was worth far more than it is now, domestic wages were miserably low and so constituted a temptation to dishonesty. Finally it was not until many years later that nursing, for men and women, became a recognised and accredited profession. There were "Sairey Gamps" and "Betsy Prigs" down to and even after the times of Charles Dickens.

Another most vicious and indeed cruel custom was the practice of the young "man about town" to visit Bethlem and to amuse himself by exciting the patients and sometimes stimulating them with drink. No one would accuse the respectable John Evelyn of intentional cruelty, but in his diary he recorded that on the 21st April, 1657: "I waited on my Lord Hatton with whom I dined; at my return I stepped into Bedlam where I saw several poor miserable creatures in chains; one of them was mad with making verses."

Gradually, however, conditions improved. The Governors were begged to pay surprise visits to see how the inmates were treated, the doors were locked on Sundays and holidays and no one was allowed to enter except on duty. It was forbidden to bring in strong drink. In 1662 a Matron was appointed and efforts were made to keep men and women patients apart.

Eventually the Governors decided that the old hospital in Bishopsgate (part of the site of Liverpool Street Station) was too old and too small, and in such a ruinous condition that they must rebuild elsewhere. A new hospital was begun in 1675 and finished in 1676. This also was visited by Evelyn who wrote in April 1678: "I went to see new Bedlam Hospital, magnificently built, and most sweetly placed in Moorfields."[1]

In this building men were in the upper and women in the lower storey with cells opening on wide galleries where visitors still amused themselves by mocking the patients through the hatches in their doors. Casual and indiscriminate visiting was still allowed and the reforms attempted some twenty years earlier do not appear to have been effective, for visitors still went to Bethlem on public holidays much as they went to the Tower of London or to the other sights of London. This practice revolted many thoughtful and humane persons and protests were made in vain to the Governors for more than a century. In the original appeal asking for support for the new hospital there is little doubt that, despite the tribute to the work of Bethlem, the abuses there were partly the cause of

[1] Later it was written of Bethlem that "pomp reigned without and misery within".

3

the foundation of that hospital, later named St. Luke's, and the rules drawn up for the hospital aimed, as will be seen, at putting an end to them.

Nevertheless, it must not be forgotten that Bethlem blazed a trail and that much was learned there. One of the most notable superintendents of St. Luke's, Thomas Dunston, who was Master and subsequently Superintendent from 1782 to 1830, was trained at Bethlem. Dunston and his wife, the Matron of St. Luke's, achieved European reputations for themselves and the hospital.

On the 13th June, 1750, six gentlemen of the City of London met at the Kings Arms Tavern in Exchange Alley to discuss a project for the establishment of a hospital as a further provision for poor lunatics. They were:

Dr. Thomas Crowe, M.D. (in the Chair),
Mr. James Sperling, Merchant of Mincing Lane,
Mr. Richard Speed, Druggist of Old Fish Street,
Mr. Thomas Light, Merchant of Mincing Lane,
Mr. William Prowting, Apothecary of Tower Street,
     and
Mr. Francis Magnus.

It is interesting to speculate whether any of the original founders were influenced by what had happened in Dublin where Dean Swift, on his death in 1745, had left his fortune to build a hospital to take in "as many idiots and lunatics" as the income would maintain. This was St. Patrick's Hospital, begun in 1748. But there is no evidence to connect the two hospitals. What is certain is that the hospital in London was an early example of London's voluntary institutions supported by contributions from the general public. It did not derive from any monastic foundation, nor from any single benefactor, but from a large number of contributors among whom the majority were probably plain well-to-do citizens and merchants, like the original six founders, moved by pity for their suffering fellow citizens. Who was the moving spirit among them is not known, but it is likely that Dr. Crowe and Mr. Sperling, two of the first Vice-Presidents, and Mr. Prowting, Treasurer from 1773 until his death in 1794, were prominent.

Mr. Sperling and Mr. Speed were two of the original three trustees, Mr. John Henry Martin being the third.

4

At this meeting the following paper was drawn up. As this was the basis on which St. Luke's Hospital was created, it is here quoted in full:

"CONSIDERATIONS upon the usefulness and necessity of establishing an Hospital, by subscription, as a further provision for Poor Lunatics.

"Notwithstanding that this Metropolis does already abound with Hospitals and Infirmaries, calculated for the relief of almost every distemper attending the poor; yet it is much to be wished that this sort of charity could be extended one step farther, by encouraging a design to establish an Hospital for the immediate reception and cure of Poor Lunatics.

"We have indeed already the hospital of Bethlem, a noble and extensive charity from which the public have as much benefit as can be reasonably expected; but it is well known that this hospital is incapable of receiving and maintaining the great number of melancholy objects of this sort who apply for relief; and that this is a truth we appeal to every Governor of that house and to every person who has had occasion to apply for the admission of a patient into it, the compassing of which is generally the work of several weeks, and indeed unavoidably so from the great numbers upon the list.

"Such, therefore, as cannot be received must either want the proper and necessary means of cure, or it must be procured for them at an expense which people in mean circumstances cannot bear.

"The usefulness and necessity of hospitals for poor lunatics is evident, for there is no disease to which human nature is subject so terrible in its appearances or so fatal in its consequences; those who are melancholy often do violence to themselves, and those who are raving, to others, and too often to their nearest relations and friends, the only persons who can be expected to take the trouble of these unhappy objects upon them.

"The law has made no particular provision for lunatics, and it must be allowed that the common parish work-houses (the inhabitants whereof are mostly aged and infirm people) are very unfit places for the reception of such ungovernable and mischievous persons, who necessarily require separate apartments.

5

"Persons afflicted with other diseases are admitted without delay into one or other of our hospitals, but persons afflicted with this worst of all diseases are not admitted into any hospital but Bethlem (probably on account of the safety of the other patients), a small limited number into Mr. Guy's only excepted.

"Would it not, therefore, be a most useful and necessary charity to establish an Hospital where such unhappy persons may be immediately admitted, and have the proper means of cure early administered to them, which are found most effectual when the patients are under the management of strangers, and by which many fatal accidents may be prevented.

"If we may judge of the probability of success in this undertaking, by the great spirit of charity and generosity that has lately attended the setting on foot some other hospitals, it may be fairly concluded that whenever a proper scheme for this purpose is offered to the public it will meet with suitable encouragement.

"We, whose names are hereunto subscribed, are of opinion that the charity here proposed is much wanted, and that there should be a meeting of such persons as are inclined to favour it, in order to consider of a proper method of setting it on foot.

"(signed) Thomas Crowe, M.D.
James Sperling
Richard Speed
Thomas Light
Francis Magnus
Wm. Prowting"

This paper having been read it was agreed to open a subscription list and that as soon as the sum of £1,000 had been promised there should be a meeting of the subscribers to elect a president, a treasurer and a secretary.

On the 29th June there was a further meeting of twelve gentlemen interested in the project. They were told that six apothecaries of the City were willing to supply the proposed hospital with drugs and medicines and to compound and dispense them as necessary, free of charge, for the next three years. These six gentlemen were in consequence declared to be subscribers and Governors for life.

It was agreed at this meeting that the paper already quoted

setting forth the necessity for establishing the proposed
hospital should be printed and circulated and subscription lists
opened, and that there should be a further meeting as soon as
£1,200 had been promised.

The project was well received by the public and sufficient
donations were promised to enable the promoters to "carry
their design into execution" and in the autumn of 1750 meetings
were held at which 3 Trustees, a Committee of 21 and a
Secretary, Mr. Thomas Webster, were appointed.

The Committee were authorised to print and circulate the
paper already quoted with such additions as they considered
desirable. They added the following narrative:

"About the beginning of June 1750 the foregoing considerations, then in writing, were perused and subscribed
by several gentlemen who on the 13th of the same month
met together to consider the usefulness, necessity and proper
method of establishing an hospital of this sort.

"At this meeting it was proposed and agreed to that a
Subscription should be opened for taking in all such sums as
well disposed persons may be inclined to contribute for that
purpose; and that every person who should subscribe and
pay into the hands of the Treasurer, to be hereafter chosen
by the subscribers, the sum of Twenty Guineas and upwards,
or Five Guineas, and agree to pay the same sum yearly for
four other successive years, should be a Governor for life;
it was also agreed that several copies of the foregoing
'considerations' should be made that by consulting other
gentlemen it might be found whether any and what objections could be made to this proposal; and as several gentlemen who were consulted declared themselves ready to join in
promoting this work, another Meeting was called where it
was agreed, in order to make this proposal more public, that
the paper entitled 'Considerations' etc. should forthwith
be printed and dispersed and also that Books should be
provided that Gentlemen and Ladies might set down what
sums they were willing to contribute to this Charity.

"That nothing of this sort might be offered to the public
which upon the strictest Examination should be found either
useless, unnecessary, or that was not likely to be attended
with success, care has been taken to enquire whether any

objections were made to this design since the printing and dispersing of the foregoing Considerations, but no material objection has been made; on the contrary many gentlemen have since that time subscribed liberally to it, and it seems to have met with general approbation.

"The principal end of establishing hospitals is that the expense is lessened by providing for a number together. The necessity, therefore, of establishing another hospital for lunatics is evident, not only as they are incapable of providing for themselves and families, are not admitted into other hospitals, or capable of being relieved (as in other diseases) by private Charity; but also as there must be servants peculiarly qualified, and every patient must have a separate room, and diet, most of them equal to persons in health.

"From hence it appears that the expenses necessarily attending the confinement and other means of cure are such as people born in middling circumstances cannot bear, it generally requiring several months, and often a whole year, before a cure is completed; so that many persons who could easily support themselves for the same length of time under any other Disease, do not apply for and are indeed proper objects to receive benefit of a Charity of this sort, and whose families without such assistance must sink under the expense.

"Although the only end hereby proposed was to establish a *Charity for poor Lunatics* in such a manner that hereafter all persons who shall be found proper objects may, for the sake of the Public as well as themselves, be admitted without delay and (should our success answer our expectations) without expense also; yet some advantages of a very interesting nature to the good of all mankind certainly will arise in consequence of it; for more Gentlemen of the Faculty, making this branch of Physick their particular care and study, it may from thence reasonably be expected that the Cure of this Dreadful Disease will hereafter be rendered more certain and expeditious, as well as less expensive; and from the many improvements already made in other Arts and Sciences as well as in the several parts of Physick, the same may, with reason, be concluded in the present instance.

"The number of Hospitals and Infirmaries of late years set up, made it necessary to consider whether this Charity might not be joined to some other, and thereby prevent a further increase, but as the apartments, attendants, and indeed every other accommodation for Lunatics, are different from those of other hospitals, and it being thought most conducive to the Public benefit that subscribers only should become Governors of this Charity, it therefore, was judged best to begin this work by itself, and we cannot but flatter ourselves from the Approbation and Success that this proposal has hitherto met with, that the charitable and benevolent disposition of the inhabitants of these Cities and the Kingdom in general will extend itself to the furtherance of this necessary undertaking.

"This design owes its Rise and Progress singly to a desire of beginning a Charity of which it must be allowed, the Public has long stood in great need, and to which many well disposed persons have declared themselves willing to contribute, and not to any motive of opposition, prejudice or private interest, and all possible care will be taken in this establishment and future direction of this Charity, to prevent an abuse of that or any other kind."

In October 1750 the Committee presented their first report to a General Meeting of the subscribers which assembled on the 10th October at the Kings Arms Tavern in the Exchange Alley.

In this they stated that they had advertised for a suitable building, but in the meanwhile had inspected one known as the Foundry in Windmill Hill, Upper Moorfields, of which the lease, held from the City of London, was about to expire. They had asked Mr. George Dance, the City Surveyor, to help them in their inspection and to make a plan of the ground. Subsequently, in explaining his plan and showing how the building could be repaired and altered to suit patients, Mr. Dance said that he was in warm sympathy with the project and he would work for it without fee or reward. This offer, needless to say, was gratefully accepted by the Governors.

At this point it will be convenient to tell what is known of the first St. Luke's Hospital.

Since the Committee had not heard of any building as suitable for their hospital as the Foundry, they were authorised by the General Meeting to make an immediate application to the City of London for a lease of the place, and in November 1750 the Court of Common Council agreed to let the Foundry and some small houses adjoining for a fine of £100 and a yearly rent of £10 for the remainder of the time that the City had the disposal of these premises, namely 32 years from the coming Christmas. The Court agreed further that, in case the City renewed their possession of the Foundry from the Prebend of the Manor of Finsbury, the Petitioners might renew their lease without paying any additional fine as they were acting for "a Charity of Public Utility".

The Foundry was a large building where formerly cannon had been cast. It had been established by Maximilian Western in 1684. Twenty years later it was leased to Matthew Bagley who took over Western's contracts with the Government and continued to cast cannon during and until the end of the Duke of Marlborough's campaigns.

In 1716, Bagley attempted to cast an extra large gun out of captured material in the presence of a distinguished company. He had, however, miscalculated the danger of the operation which resulted in a violent explosion. In this Bagley himself and several others were killed and many of the onlookers were injured.

Subsequently it was leased to John Wesley[1] as a place for preaching, and for many years was the centre of his operations.

In 1740 it was described by Silas Todd as a ruinous place with a pantile covering, a few rough boards put together to constitute a temporary pulpit and several other decayed timbers comprising the whole structure. If this is correct it would seem that Mr. Wesley had not expended any large sum on repairs and that the Foundry still showed signs of the explosion of 1716.

When the lease was granted to the Committee, Mr. Wesley begged to be allowed to continue for the time being to meet at the Foundry as he was without any other place where he and his followers could assemble. Some of the occupants of the adjoining small houses also begged for an extension of time before they were evicted at the end of the year. Clearly housing was a problem 200 years ago.

To these petitions the Committee gave favourable replies.

---

[1] Some authorities state that it was bought by Wesley and that he spent a considerable sum on repairing it, but the Minutes of the Hospital state most definitely that the place was leased from the City of London. On the site of the Foundry, i.e., the West end of Worship Street, houses were built in later years, and the name of Providence Row, retained until comparatively recently, was given to them.

They told Mr. Wesley that they were unwilling to distress him, particularly as all the buildings of the group would not be wanted for some months, adding that they hoped that if he received any favour from them he would return it to the charity. It is pleasant to record that, when Mr. Wesley's stewards, a few months later, asked for a further extension of time, they enclosed in their letter a cheque for £7 10s. od. in token of their gratitude.

As a result of a further and more detailed examination of the premises by the Committee and Mr. Dance, it is not surprising to learn that in the opinion of the Surveyor the building was so old that the necessary alterations could not be done by contract and that it would be best to entrust the work to "men of ability and integrity", to be carried out by what would now be described as direct labour.

Accordingly, having satisfied themselves that Mr. Robert Taylor, carpenter, and Mr. Jasper Horne, bricklayer, had the qualities stipulated by Mr. Dance, they and other tradesmen were selected and were instructed to begin work after Christmas with as many labourers as could be employed on the premises.

What exactly were the design and amenities of the first hospital is not known. All that exists is an outline sketch of what appears to be the principal front but without any main entrance. John Noorthouch in his *History of London* 1773 describes it thus: "at the north-west corner of Moorfields stands St. Luke's hospital for Lunatics, a neat but very plain edifice; nothing here is expended in ornament and we only see a building of considerable length, plastered over and whitened, with ranges of small square windows on which no decorations have been bestowed. Adjoining to the North side of this hospital is an old building called the Foundry, now a meeting-house under the direction of the Rev. John Wesley."

The new hospital was given its name "St. Luke's" in June 1751. It was situated in St. Luke's parish and in any case this was an appropriate name for a hospital. As altered, and whether it included the Foundry or not, it would appear to have fulfilled the conditions considered desirable in the middle of the eighteenth century for a Hospital for Lunatics, namely something between a monastery and a gaol with the disadvantages of both institutions. Of course, in the case of those who could pay for their treatment in private asylums the amenities there must have been greater. The charges in such establishments were probably relatively high, for Dr. Battie, St. Luke's first physician (who had his own private asylum) died, according to Horace Walpole, worth £100,000, a very large sum in those days.

For poor lunatics, however, security rather than comfort was considered essential. Though there was little comfort at St. Luke's according to the standard of the times, the medical treatment was first class, and the general care and feeding were good of their kind. Consequently, the patients there may be assumed to have been less miserable than in the majority of buildings that housed these unfortunate sufferers in those days.

How far the condition of the Foundry had been improved since the report of 1740 is not known. It is likely that some alterations had been made, but it is evident that this ancient building, like all old constructions, presented considerable structural difficulties. However, the work seems to have been carried out very expeditiously by the "men of ability and integrity", for in July 1751, eight months after the work had begun, a few patients were admitted, and by January 1752 the Committee reported that the hospital had been altered and equipped for 26 patients and 3 resident servants and that the following bills had been paid:

	£	s.	d.		£	s.	d.
Carpenter . .	500	4	0	Cabinet-Maker .	6	12	0
Bricklayer . .	359	5	0	Upholsterer .	35	0	0
Smith . .	76	5	0	Printer . .	58	2	0
Plumber . .	66	6	0	Coal Merchant .	15	5	0
Mason . .	32	7	0	Stationer . .	6	4	0
Plasterer . .	63	19	6	Brewer . .	13	7	0
Ironmonger .	46	0	0	Butcher . .	15	12	0
Painter . .	38	18	0	Cheesemonger .	7	11	0
Glazier . .	29	0	0	Baker . .	11	19	0
Labourer . .	18	17	0	Servants' Wages	34	3	4
Tarring part of the				Rent . .	10	1	4
Hospital .	4	11	0	Sundry Expenses	33	0	6
Bedding . .	32	0	0	Petty Expenses .	23	12	0
Linen . .	21	15	0				
Turnery Ware .	19	15	0		£1,681	15	8
Pair of Scales .	4	18	0				
Smoke Jack .	6	6	0				

Another bill that was paid later in 1752 was one of £13 for making and fixing a cold bath, regarding which there appears to have been some misunderstanding as the tradesman responsible was called before the Committee for explanations. The sudden and unexpected immersion in a cold bath was part of the treatment in those days and for many years afterwards.

There is no plan or information to show what were the interior arrangements of the first St. Luke's Hospital. A note in an early minute mentions that the Committee were authorised to make such arrangements as they thought fit in the several rooms between the kitchen and the hall, and there were other minutes from time to time to the effect that more "cells" were to be fitted up.

In 1754 the Committee recommended that, as there was only one common room in the hospital for all the patients, and that as the number of patients had increased considerably since the opening, another room should be provided so that men and women patients could be kept separate. This was approved by the General Court.

Judging from the outline sketch of the "Foundry-Hospital" as well as from the gaol-like design of the much improved hospital built in 1782-84, this first hospital must have been an unspeakably gloomy and depressing place with few and small windows which were almost certainly heavily barred and therefore almost impossible to keep clean.

Nevertheless, its success was immediate, both as regards charitable donations and in demands for admission, the former making it possible to carry out the extensions which the latter made desirable.

While the hospital was being built, a special sub-Committee was appointed to draw up rules and regulations for its government, and, in the words of Dr. William Rawes who wrote a short history of St. Luke's in 1904, when he was Medical Superintendent, "so carefully were these thought out that, except for a few additions and some slight alterations in minor details, they held good for 100 years". Indeed, many of them were in force when he wrote.

It is unnecessary to quote them in full, but they dealt with the procedure and duties of General Courts and Committees and of House Committees, election of officers, auditing of accounts and so forth.

Some of them are, however, worthy of note when the somewhat easy principles of patronage that obtained in those days
are remembered. They are evidence that the Governors
recognised that there were features in the administration and
discipline of Bethlem that were undesirable and must not be
allowed in St. Luke's.

In the preamble they reiterated their reasons for appealing
to the public for support and contributions. They mentioned the
difficulty and expense of being received into Bethlem and the
advantages of having a new hospital administered by its own
Governors and of the prospect of interesting more "Gentlemen
of the Faculty" in the study of lunacy, the knowledge of which
for too long had been confined "almost to a single person".

It was laid down that purchases should be made when
possible by contract. But no contract was to be made in which
a member of the Committee was concerned.

Patients were not to be exposed to public view.

The Physician and Surgeon were to attend the hospital every
weekly House Committee day and as often otherwise as
necessary, but at least on one other day in the week. The same
applied to the six apothecaries who had offered their drugs
free, in monthly rotation.

No Physician or Surgeon might officiate in place of the
regular physician or surgeon without permission from the
General or House Committee.

The senior servants, i.e., the Man and Woman Keeper, were
to be responsible for receiving the provisions and their daily
distribution to patients, for locking and unlocking the doors, for
general care of the house, and for seeing that no strong drinks,
tea or provisions of any kind were brought to the patients from
outside.

The Messenger or Porter was to prevent any patient from
going out and to report to the Keeper if any stranger wished to
come into the hospital.

The maid servants, later known as "gallery maids", were to
clean the house daily before 10 a.m., dress the victuals, and
wash and assist in the care of the patients."

All servants were to be diligent in complying with the order
of the Keepers and other superiors, and to "behave themselves
properly to the patients and with civility and respect to all
strangers."

Any servant who took any fee, gratuity or reward from any tradesman, patient or friend of a patient, was to be discharged forthwith.

Neither the Porter nor maid servants were to go out of the hospital without leave of the Keepers, and both the Keepers were not to be absent at the same time.

A visitors' book was to be kept in some public and convenient place wherein the Governors were to enter any complaints of neglect or misconduct by officers or servants in order that they might be considered and redressed by the Committee.

The instructions issued to persons who applied for the admission of a patient stated:

"That no person shall knowingly be received as a patient into this hospital who is not in point of circumstances a proper object of this charity—that is, poor and mad." Those who had suffered from lunacy for more than twelve months duration, or had been discharged uncured from another institution for lunatics, idiots, persons suffering from epileptic or convulsive fits or venereal disease, and pregnant women were declared to be ineligible. "And every such person who through mistake or mis-information shall be received into this hospital shall be discharged immediately on a discovery of any of the above disqualifications."

They went on to state:

"Therefore, if the patient is not disqualified by any of the above rules, upon application the forms of two printed certificates, together with a petition, may be had, the first of which certificates (after it is filled up) must be signed by the minister and church-wardens or overseer of the poor of the parish, and the other by some physicians, surgeon or apothecary who hath visited such patient; after which the person or persons who saw them sign must go before one of His Majesty's Justices of the Peace, or some other person authorised to take affidavits, and make oath in a manner as is printed at the bottom of the certificates."

The certificates had then to be signed by a Governor, and together with the petition, left with the secretary for registration. The petitioner was required to attend the next meeting of the House Committee when the certificates were examined and, if approved, an order was made for the patient to be brought for examination by the House Committee in his turn.

. The petitioner had also to find two substantial householders residing within the "bills of mortality" to enter into a bond of £100 to remove the patient when discharged. No Governor could be security for any patient.

Any patient who had been for 12 months in the hospital and showed no sign of improvement was discharged.

It is clear that the Governors aimed at creating a hospital where the patients could be cured and at first this rule was observed strictly. Some years later incurable, or rather un-cured, patients were re-admitted on payment of a weekly fee of five shillings.

These elaborate and strict rules sometimes caused trouble, but the Governors were determined that they should be observed. To give but one instance: not long after the hospital was opened the following letter was sent to the Minister of the Parish of St. Giles, Cripplegate:

"Sir, I am directed by the Committee of St. Luke's Hospital for Lunatics to inform you that the petition on behalf of M.B. was this day rejected, it appearing that you had signed the certificate thereunto annexed before the same was filled up, and that the Churchwardens, after your example, had done the like. They hope this will be a caution to you for the future not to mislead ignorant people and impose upon the Committee.

"I am, your humble servant,
"Thomas Webster."

The Minister accepted the rebuke, signed a fresh certificate and the patient was admitted a fortnight later.

These Rules were finally approved at a General Meeting in 1751.

By this time the Rt. Hon. the Earl of Cardigan,[1] afterwards

[1] George Brudenell-Montagu was the eldest son of the third Earl of Cardigan. Born in 1712, he succeeded his father in 1732. He married Lady Mary Montagu, third daughter and co-heiress of the second Duke of Montagu. He took the name and arms of his wife and in 1766 was created Duke of Montagu. His only and somewhat doubtful titles to fame were that in 1762 he was made a Knight of the Garter, this being the first investiture of a subject *in absentia*, and that he was Governor to the Prince of Wales, afterwards George IV. On his death the Dukedom became extinct.

Duke of Montagu, had accepted the Presidency, an office to which he was re-elected each year until his death in 1790.

The four first Vice-Presidents elected were Sir James Lowther, Bart., John Joliffe, Esq., Dr. Thomas Crowe and James Sperling, Esq., the two last named being among the original founders.

Mr. William Davy was appointed to be the first Treasurer.

Among the early resolutions recommended by the General Committee and approved by the Court, was the following: "That the Governors do dine together at five shillings each, the exceedings to be paid by the Stewards, and that the Committee do appoint ten Stewards who shall deliver out tickets to the Governors and their friends, and that no French wine be drunk at such Meetings."

This resolution was passed annually for the next ninety-five years with an increase in the price of the tickets from time to time, but always with the same restrictions in the matter of French wines. The dinner was originally an occasion for collecting subscriptions, but in 1767 the Court agreed that such collection should no longer be made.

The first physician of St. Luke's, appointed in October 1750, was Dr. William Battie, who was an outstanding figure in the medical world of those days, and who, in 1764, was elected President of the College of Physicians. According to Dr. Rawes, his ideas were at least 50 years in advance of his generation, and doubtless his double experience at his own private asylum and at St. Luke's Hospital may have contributed to his skill. The *Dictionary of National Biography* describes him as an "eccentric humorist".

The following is an example of one of his weekly reports to the House Committee. In the Minutes it is recorded that he acquainted the Committee that "J.S., after a long trial, discovers no other sign of lunacy than incurable obstinacy which may rather be imputed to perverseness of temper than to bodily disorder capable of being relieved by medicine." The patient was accordingly brought before the Committee and, after examination, discharged.

In his *Treatise on Madness*, 1758, Dr. Battie wrote that very little was known by the ordinary medical man about its treatment "except he may perchance have heard of antimonial vomits, strong purges and hellebore as specifically antimaniacal, which traditional knowledge, however, if indiscriminately practised, would soon make him wish he had never heard of them."

Of the causes of madness he mentioned alcohol, and "the bottle companions . . . who drink till they see double and then drink till they cannot see at all"; overwork, as exemplified by "infirm and shattered philosophers who, after having spent many days and nights without closing their eyes in unwearied endeavours to reconcile metaphysical contradictions, square the circle, etc., may, without a metaphor, be said to have cracked their brains."

He also mentions gluttony, causing the megrim of the epicure, and idleness, causing the temptations of St. Anthony or the ecstasies of "sedentary and chlorotic nuns and their frequent conversations with angelic ministers of grace. Not to mention what now and then happens to the senior recluses in our Protestant Monasteries at Oxford and Cambridge."

He also referred to hereditary madness instanced by "the striking oddities that characterise whole families, derived from lunatic ancestors, and the frequent breaking forth of real madness in the offspring of such ill-concerted alliances, and that from little or no provocation strongly intimate that the nerves in such persons are not originally formed perfect and like the nerves of other men."

He deprecated the lowering treatment generally recommended in those days, and preferred tonics and treatment for the general health, including sea-bathing and fresh air.

On the other hand it is clear that he admitted a certain amount of restraint, for such restraint, where patients were fastened by a belt or other means to their bed or a chair, was mentioned in their reports by the Commissioners in Lunacy 100 years later. By then, however, restraint was limited to only a few patients. In these early years handcuffs and leg logs were also in use, and in 1750 sanction was given for the purchase of 12 pairs of the former and 12 single leg logs.

The first Surgeon appointed was Mr. J. Sheron. Nothing is known of his qualifications or experience. He died in 1755.

The diet of the patients was presumably good compared to what they would have got in their own homes, but to our modern ideas it appears not only lamentably dull, but in many respects deficient. The only items recorded in the Minutes and the receipted bills were:

Bread:	Second quality at from 3d. to 7d. per peck (17 lbs. 6 oz.), under the assize, that is to say on an average 1s. for a half peck loaf of 8 lb. 11 oz.
Flour:	At the same price.
Oatmeal:	At 4s. 6d. to 5s. per bushel of 56 lb.
Butter:	Average price 5½d. per lb.
Cheese:	„ „ 2¾d. to 3d. per lb.
Beef and Mutton:	At 1s. 10d. to 2s. 4d. per stone of 8 lb.
Small Beer:	At 14s. or 15s. a barrel.

Neither potatoes nor any form of vegetable nor tea, milk nor sugar are ever mentioned in the Minutes or the receipted bills.

Dr. Battie gave it as his opinion that "Veal was unnecessary and Pork improper" for the patients. The first presumably because they would be eating "above their station", and the latter because it would not be good for them.

Within the limits of this diet the rations given to the patients seem to have been liberal. It is nowhere stated what they actually were, but by comparing the actual bills with the average number of patients and attendants, the average daily ration for the years 1751 to 1760 works out as follows:

Bread or Flour:	From 7 to 10 oz.
Oatmeal:	About 2 oz.
Cheese or Butter:	„ „
Beef or Mutton:	Just under ½ lb.*
Small Beer	

The annual cost of feeding a patient was between £5 and £7 according to actual receipted bills.

The house expenses were, of course, higher; it is nowhere recorded what they included, but presumably wages, coal and other miscellaneous items. During the first ten years the cost per patient ranged from £9 4s. to £12 10s. The cost of the incurables was higher than that of the ordinary patient, their

*It should be remembered that the quantity of meat consumed by the average well-to-do individual at this period was enormous.

house expenses varying between £12 10s. and £13 per annum. But these were always balanced by their fees.

It is not possible to give more exact figures as the audited figures which were drawn up each year by a panel of Governors, although set forth very clearly, were not produced on the lines of a modern balance sheet. They did not differentiate, for instance, between genuine repairs, maintenance, extensions, etc., necessitated by the increase of patients, or carried out as the result of experience; that is to say, between current and capital expenditure.

It is clear, however, that the value and necessity of the hospital, as evidenced by charitable donations and subscriptions and demands for admission, were at once recognised, and the steady increase in the donations received enabled the Governors not only to carry out extensions but to build up and invest a large general fund.

Between 1751 and 1761, thanks to the careful management of the General Committee, the clear estate of the hospital was increased from £8,188 to £16,995.

The number of patients rose from 24 in February 1752 to 57 in February 1753. In 1754 it was decided to re-admit incurable patients and from that time till February 1761 the numbers remained steady at about 50 curable and 20 incurable patients.

In the first ten years of its existence, 749 patients had been received into the hospital; of these 363 had been discharged cured, 198 uncured, 61 as idiots, 33 at the desire of their friends, 3 for want of necessary clothing and 1 as an improper object of the Charity; 39 had died.

At first the only attendants considered necessary were a head man Keeper and a head female Keeper, assisted by two men and two women attendants. The head Keepers were husband and wife, and were paid between them £30 a year. In addition, they received respectively gratuities of £10 and £6. These two had received some training at Bethlem. The two women attendants did all the cooking and housework in addition to looking after the patients. They received £10 a year and gratuities of £4. All of them, including the head Keepers, received free board and lodging. None of these attendants had any special training but some of them may have had experience in Bethlem or elsewhere. There is no reason, however, to think that such experience was considered essential. About 25 per cent. were illiterate and unable to sign the receipts for their wages, save by making their mark.

Altogether the arrangements at St. Luke's Hospital were, according to modern ideas, extremely primitive, but even so they were in advance of general practice, and the results achieved in the circumstances are impressive.

II

THE GROWTH OF THE HOSPITAL AND THE MOVE
TO OLD STREET

UNTIL 1786 St. Luke's Hospital remained at Windmill Hill. It was a time of steady growth in numbers, experience and financial strength. The Governors seem to have hoped that they would be able to keep their original site and they offered either to rent it on a long lease or to buy it together with an extension, which would give them an area with a frontage of 480 and a depth of 300 feet. But the Committee of City Lands would neither agree to a lease of 91 years at an annual rent of £140, nor to a purchase of the fee simple and inheritance for £4,260 or even £5,000. They wanted more, and there the matter dropped as far as the original site was concerned.

By 1780 the hospital accommodated on an average 80 curable and 30 incurable patients, but the Governors were anxious to help a larger number. This shortly became well within the scope of their funds, for in 1767 Sir Thomas Clarke, Master of the Rolls, in his will left the Charity a handsome donation of £30,000 and the clear estate, i.e., the funds of the hospital, rose from £23,782 to £56,889. Consequently, although the annual house expenses had risen from about £700 in 1752 to an average of £1,500 in 1780, the careful Governors kept well within their income and were able each year to invest a large proportion of the donations they received.

When the negotiations for the Windmill Hill site came to nothing, the search for a convenient alternative was resumed, and in 1776 the Committee reported that the Governors of St. Bartholomew's Hospital were prepared to grant them a lease of about three acres of ground immediately north of Old Street Road. Before, however, giving the details of this property or the terms of the lease, some of the changes in the staff and the system of administration that took place between 1751 and 1786, when the new hospital was completed and occupied, must be mentioned.

22

In 1764 Dr. Battie resigned the appointment of consulting physician.[1] He had been appointed President of the College of Physicians that year and possibly this may have prevented him from giving his time to the hospital. He was succeeded by Dr. Thomas Brooke, who held this position until his death in 1781.

On the indirect evidence of the physicians' centenary report both Drs. Battie and Brooke were believers in medical treatment. Their successor, on the same evidence, had less faith in medicine compared to moral treatment. He was Dr. Samuel Foart Simmons who was appointed Physician on the death of Dr. Brooke. He came from the Westminster General Dispensary and became one of the best known of the physicians who dealt with insanity. He was elected a Fellow of the Royal Society and in 1803 George III was entrusted to his care. In 1811 he was again in attendance when the King became permanently insane, and it was in this year that he resigned from St. Luke's after holding the appointment for 30 years.

The Governors were fortunate in their servants. Mr. Thomas Webster, his son John, and his grandson Thomas, between them held the post of Secretary for just under 100 years from 1750 to 1849.

Mr. Mansfield, the "Keeper" (as the head male attendant was styled until 1786 when his title was changed to "Master"), after 30 years of faithful service, resigned for reasons of ill-health in 1781. He and his wife, Mary, were succeeded by Mr. and Mrs. Pearson, who were dismissed after six months for various misdemeanours which included the acceptance of bribes, changing tradesmen who had served the hospital well,

---

[1] "Letter of resignation from Dr. William Battie.   April 4th, 1764
"My Lords and Gentlemen,

"Improvement in medical knowledge being one of the principal objects of Hospital practice for which men growing old in confirmed habits and opinions are not so well qualified, I cannot at present answer your good intentions better than by retiring from this part of the mad business in time, and resigning the care of your patients to some younger physician.

"Though the connection with which you have so highly honoured for more than thirteen years is hereby dissolved, give me leave to assure you that I think myself bound as much as ever by the strictest ties of humanity as well as a particular gratitude and attention, to wish well to the prosperity of so useful a charity and, as long as I live, shall gladly lay hold of every opportunity of promoting its interest.

"I am, with the greatest respect,
"Your much obliged and faithful servant,
"(sgd.) W. Battie."

23

and appointing others "of their own acquaintance". They had also allowed patients to go out of the hospital with their friends without any reference to the physician, and finally instead of burning waste and foul straw they had used it to make a dunghill and had converted the incinerator into a "hogstye".

In 1782 Mr. Thomas Dunston and his wife were appointed head man and woman Keeper respectively. They came from Bethlem, where they had been for 8 years, and remained at St. Luke's for 48 years. During that time they established for the hospital and themselves a European reputation, according to an early number of the *Journal of Mental Science*.

The stay of the Surgeons and the resident Apothecaries (who eventually became the Medical Superintendents) was usually much shorter, but they and the Governors usually parted with expressions of mutual esteem, many of them being elected Governors on their resignation. Only in the case of one apothecary—John Harris—were there any complaints. It was reported that he frequently left the hospital in the forenoon and did not return again until after one o'clock in the morning and then "most commonly much disguised in liquor", and that on such occasions he never told anyone in the hospital where he was to be found in case of emergency. Needless to say, when the General Court heard the report of the Committee, they discharged Mr. Harris without delay. His case, however, was quite exceptional.

The long service of the Mansfields, the Dunstons and the three generations of Websters is testimony of the good relations and mutual esteem between the Governors and their servants, and of the spirit of loyalty to the hospital that must have existed, and which indeed has always been a feature not only of St. Luke's but of all hospitals in this country. Long service may, however, sometimes have its disadvantages and result occasionally in a certain rigidity of outlook and practice, particularly when, as in the case of St. Luke's, some of the Consulting Physicians on the medical and several of the Treasurers on the administrative side held their posts for many years. The deliberation with which, in the middle of the nineteenth century, changes were made in St. Luke's, not only on the recommendations of the Commissioners in Lunacy but of their own Medical Officers, is perhaps an indication of such conservatism.

As regards the diet of the patients, there does not seem to have been much change during this period. In 1761 the Committee deferred making any contract for butter and cheese "on account of the considerable rise on those articles owing to the great demand for furnishing the Navy", and agreed with their previous contractor that he should supply the hospital on the best terms possible. This arrangement was continued for the next eight years until 1769, when they paid 6½d. per lb. for butter, and 3½d. for cheese, but after that year they had to revert to their previous arrangement and buy at the market prices.

In 1769 it was found that the bread and flour were not up to previous standards, and the Committee decided to buy flour as required and to have the bread baked by a baker who would be supplied with flour by the hospital. The proposal actually made by the baker in 1784 and accepted by the Committee, was that he should bake the hospital bread at the price of 5s. for each sack of flour, each sack to make 41 half peck loaves of 139 oz. each. This arrangement was copied from a similar one in force at Bethlem. It gave the patients and staff about 20 oz. of bread daily, a more liberal allowance than in the years 1751-61, but as the quantities in each case are based on receipted bills which are the only available figures, they cannot be regarded as anything more than approximate.

The price of meat rose from 1s. 9d. a stone of 8 lb. in the years 1762-65 to over 2s. In 1770, and again in 1780, it was 2s. 4d. and between these years it rose as high as 2s. 9d. and never fell below 2s. 1d. On one occasion the Committee were offered a contract for meat at a considerably lower price. They considered, however, that such meat would be below the standard hitherto approved, and rejected it accordingly.

The weekly meat ration in this period, however, does not seem to have been as liberal as in the previous period, and works out at about ⅓ lb. daily.

It is not possible to calculate whether the daily ration of butter and cheese was altered, but the total cost of these items was very much higher, being more than double in 1770, and in 1780 nearly three times what it was in 1761. It almost certainly remained at 2 oz. of each daily.

The number of attendants increased from 2 maids and 2 men in 1761 to 5 and 4 in 1771, and to 8 maids and 3 men in 1780. The maids continued at £8 a year with a gratuity of £4, and the men at £10 with a gratuity of £5. One maid, however, was paid £15 as assistant maid to Mrs. Mansfield and received a gratuity of £5. These wages were fairly high for the period, and in 1787, when the attendants asked for a rise, the General Committee refused it.

As already mentioned, the Governors of St. Bartholomew's Hospital had in 1776 offered to St. Luke's a lease of some three acres. These were part of their Peerless Estate on the north side of Old Street Road.

The terms of the lease were favourable and the conditions were approved by the General Court which authorised the Committee to proceed with the building of the new hospital when the lease had been completed. The agreement was signed in March 1777, and the following is an extract from a copy of the Minutes made by the Committee of St. Bartholomew's Hospital:

"Upon the proposal of Messrs. Sperling, Speed, Prowting and Pearce, four of the Governors of St. Luke's Hospital, on behalf of themselves and the Governors of the said Hospital to the Governors of this Hospital:

"It is thought fit and ordered that the Governors of St. Luke's (for the use of that Charity and for the purpose of building an hospital) shall have a lease of all that parcel of ground called The Bowling Green, a tenement heretofore called the Fox and Goose, together with several small sheds, buildings and gardens thereunto belonging, and also all that small messuage and garden lying behind the Bowling Green, which said premises are situate near Old Street in the parish of St. Luke's, Middlesex, now in the occupation of the Widdow Napper, her under-tenants or assigns, and also of all that messuage, garden and other premises now in the occupation of Thomas Harris, his under-tenants or assigns, to hold from the Feast Day of St. Michael the Arch-Angel next ensuing for the term of 42 years at the yearly rent of a pepper corn for the first two years and for the remaining 40 years at the yearly rent of £200 free and clear of the land tax, etc., with benefit of renewal at the expiration of the first 14 years for the sum of £200 by way of fine, and the like annual rent of £200 and so on regularly for ever at the expiration of every 14 years on payment of the same fine.

26

In which lease shall be contained all usual and reasonable covenants between landlords and tenants and that the Governors of St. Luke's Hospital shall expend the full sum of £10,000 at least within the first 4 years of the said term in substantial buildings, and shall insure and keep insured the Buildings for that sum.

"And in the Lease shall be contained a proviso that in case the Governors of St. Luke's shall (after they have built and completely finished the said hospital) leave any part of the ground vacant, they or their successors are at liberty to build good and substantial houses thereon provided the same be no annoyance to the other tenants of St. Bartholomews thereto adjoining. And at the end or other determination of the lease will surrender the said premises together with all fixtures."

Mr. Prowting, as Treasurer and on behalf of himself and the other Governors of St. Luke's, put a £20 bank note into the Poor Box (of St. Bartholomew's) as token of their acceptance of the Lease.

These three acres were included in a piece of ground which consisted of "6 acres of meadow with appurtenances lying . . . at Irish Field in the County of Middlesex in the parish of St. Giles without Cripplegate". This had been granted to St. Bartholomew's Hospital in a Charter of Henry VIII dated 1547. In and about this area were many pools and ponds fed by springs in the hills of Highgate and Hampstead. One of these was known as "Perilous Pool", because divers youths by swimming there had been drowned. But when, in 1743, a Mr. Kemp was given a lease of 3 acres of this estate including this particular pool, he judiciously changed its name to "Peerless", for he intended to make it an open-air swimming pool and fish-pond, and it was so used for many years afterwards.

The rest of this estate was the land leased to St. Luke's.

A special Sub-Committee was appointed to contract for and complete the building of the new hospital. In February 1778 they made their first report. They had selected Mr. George Dance, Junior, R.A., son of the designer of the "Foundry" hospital, to be their architect. He and his pupil, (afterwards the famous Sir John Soane), each submitted plans and estimates for the hospital, but the Sub-Committee thought these would cost more than they considered prudent to lay out

27

on the building, and they asked Mr. Dance to prepare another plan to cost a total of about £30,000.

There is no further record of the Sub-Committee's meetings until 1782, when they reported to the Court that they had approved of a plan which Mr. Dance estimated would cost £17,300, of which the "carcase" (presumably the main interior and exterior walls and roof), would absorb £11,000. Accordingly, they had written "to eleven different persons to send in their proposals for what sum they would contract for building the carcase of the said hospital", according to Mr. Dance's plans. Of those who tendered Messrs. Hobson, the Bricklayers of Horsly Down, put in the lowest estimate and their tender was accepted.

When trenches were opened for the foundations of the building it was found that "owing to the softness of the ground it was necessary to plank the same with fir". Mr. Dance estimated that this would cost another £300 (actually it cost £247) and he was told to get this done accordingly as well and as cheaply as possible.

At the same time the Committee reported that the President had agreed to lay the first stone of the new hospital at 2 o'clock on the 30th July. The Governors also decided to defer their annual dinner in order that, following the ceremony, they might entertain the Duke of Montagu at dinner with them at Batson's Coffee House in Cornhill, and asked all those who intended to be present to pay the Secretary £1 11s. 6d. But the Duke declined the invitation on the plea that he had to return to the King at Windsor.

However, the Governors gave him a collation of wine and fruit, and, in the presence of a large number of Governors and others, he duly laid the first stone[1] to which a copper plate with the following inscription was fixed, the whole being sealed in an envelope of lead:

"The first stone of this hospital was laid on the 30th day of July 1782 by:

[1] During subsequent alterations and additions to the hospital this stone was built over and all trace of it was lost, until the building was being altered and strengthened by the Bank of England for their printing works. It was then discovered quite by chance and returned by the Bank to the governors who received it gratefully and placed it in the entrance hall of Woodside Hospital, opened in 1930.

28

"The Most High puissant and noble prince George Brudenell-Montagu, Duke of Montagu, Marquis of Monthermer, Earl of Cardigan, Baron Brudenell of Stanton Wyvill in the County of Leicester, and Baronet; one of His Majesty's Most Honourable Privy Council, Master of the Horse to the King, Governor and Captain of Windsor Castle, F.R.S., Knight of the Most Noble Order of the Garter and President of St. Luke's Hospital for Lunatics, which was instituted in the year

1751

by voluntary subscription.

"And by the General Benefaction of the public, the Governors are now enabled to erect this Building for the reception of their patients.

"Edmund Payne, Esq.,⎫
John Elliott, Esq.,⎬ Vice-Presidents
Stephen Peter Godin, Esq.,⎭
William Prowting, Esq., Treasurer"

On this occasion a gift of ten guineas was made to the workmen who had prepared the ground and foundations.

Work on the building continued from 1782 to 1786 and on the 1st January, 1787, the patients were transferred from the old to the new hospital.

It is not possible to say exactly what was the cost of St. Luke's Hospital in Old Street. According to the existing receipted bills they paid Messrs. Hobson of Horsly Down over £22,000, Peter and John Banner, the carpenters, £8,076, and various miscellaneous tradesmen about £4,000, a total of over £38,000. But unfortunately the receipt books for the years after the middle of 1788 are missing, and therefore the sum charged against the building account in the annual audits, namely £46,000, is more likely to represent the true cost of St. Luke's Hospital.

Whatever the cost, the building was, and is, a remarkably impressive one. As will be seen from the illustration, the design is very simple, and relies for its effect on its excellent proportions and skilful arrangement of horizontal and vertical lines.

Not long ago, a writer in the *Builder* described it as amongst the finest examples of brickwork in London, the area permitting a great length of frontage and thus obviating any appearance of top-heaviness.

So proud of it were the Governors, and so anxious were the public to inspect it that it was thrown open for inspection, thereby delaying, for some three weeks, the transfer of the patients, who spent the Christmas of 1786 in the old hospital.

Both the Committee and the Court had held meetings in the Board Room of the new hospital on the 24th November, 1786.

Strictly speaking, therefore, it was no longer necessary for them to meet at various coffee-houses and taverns[1] as they had done for the last 36 years. However, for many years the General Court and Committee continued to hold their meetings at such places which were both convenient and where it was no doubt possible to obtain such refreshment as would help their deliberations.

Despite the fact that the hospital was the very latest building of its kind and was almost certainly equipped with what were then all the most modern improvements, it must have been a dreary enough building with its long gloomy corridors, into which the cells opened and from whose small wire-covered windows set high in the walls no view could be seen. Even in 1916, when it had been enormously improved, decorated, and its windows enlarged, it struck its eventual purchasers as a terribly gloomy place.

As the City grew up round it and, so to speak, engulfed it, it must have become more and more depressing, not only to the patients, who rarely left it, but to the attendants, who did occasionally get out. Security was still the first essential of a hospital for lunatics, and their medical treatment does not seem to have advanced markedly during the 36 years of St. Luke's, except that restraint was practised somewhat less and was discouraged as far as Mr. Dunston was concerned, owing, doubtless, to the principles instilled by the physicians.

Meanwhile, all the patients were safely transferred from Moorfields to Old Street and a receipted bill exists which reads: "To Thomas Lewis—To 4 Hackney Coaches at 7 o'clock morning January 1st, 1787 to remove the patients from Old

---

[1] Those most frequently mentioned were Batson's Coffee House, and the Kings Arms Tavern. Occasional meetings were held at the Stock Exchange and the Antwerp Taverns, Garraways, and the Jerusalem Coffee Houses and Pontacs. There had also been frequent meetings at the Foundry.

St. Luke's to the New Hospital . . . £1 10s. 0d. Received 30th January 1787."

So pleased were the Governors with the arrangements made by the Master and Matron that they voted them a donation of £50 and gave each servant a special bonus of £1.

In the following month, Mr. Thomas Webster, who had been Secretary for 36 years, resigned his appointment. He was voted a Governor for life and his son John was elected to succeed him.

The General Committee reported that during these 36 years 3,745 patients had been admitted, and of these 1,701 had been discharged cured, 1,231 uncured, and 228 had died. The remainder had left for various reasons, and there were in the new hospital on the occasion of their first Report, 89 curable and 30 incurable patients.

III

THE END OF THE EIGHTEENTH CENTURY
EARLY YEARS IN OLD STREET

ALTHOUGH the patients were moved from the old into the new hospital on the 1st January, 1787, the building was not completely finished until the end of the following year, when the final accounts were settled. They included a fee of £2,227 to Mr. Dance. After this settlement the principal contractors and the architect all gave a donation to the hospital, and the Committee voted Mr. Dance, Mr. William Hobson (head of the firm of bricklayers) and Mr. Banner (the carpenter) Governors for life.

Messrs. Hobson were the principal contractors and were responsible for the "carcase" of the building; the other tradesmen were not sub-contractors to them but to the Governors, and they were all paid directly by the Treasurer on certificates from Mr. Dance.

In addition to supervision by the architect it is recorded that the building Committee, some of whom doubtless were practical and experienced men, watched the hospital grow from its foundations upwards.

The Minutes make mention of certain personal matters at about this time, and they are, therefore, included here.

In August 1789 the Committee passed a resolution which was confirmed by the General Court, to the effect that as the "Charity owed its institution to William Prowting, Esq., their worthy Treasurer, he having been the first promoter thereof", and, having since shown the greatest zeal and attention to its interests, and, as they saw with great pleasure the flourishing state of the hospital, they wished to pay him the compliment of having his portrait painted for the Board Room. The expense of the picture was defrayed by the Committee, and in 1949 it hung with others in Woodside Hospital. There is no record concerning the artist or what he was paid.

In September 1787 Mr. Samuel Whitbread signified to the Treasurer his intention of securing to the Charity 100 guineas a year for ever upon condition of his being at liberty to recommend one patient for admission into the hospital and after his decease that such parish as he should name should at all times thereafter have the like power. Subsequently, this donation was secured on property owned by Mr. Whitbread's brewery, and has been paid ever since. A representative of the family has generally been a Governor, sometimes as a Vice-President and once as a President. About the same time Mr. Whitbread gave £3,000 to the Middlesex Hospital to endow a ward for Cancer cases, and so a connection between the two hospitals was established early in their history through a common benefactor.

In 1788 Mr. David Powell was elected to the General Committee and became Treasurer in 1794. He was the first of a family which ever since has played an important part in the government of St. Luke's Hospital and has provided four Treasurers covering a period of 76 years and always a member of the General Committee, and thus has given a noteworthy example of practical and hereditary charity.

The number of patients admitted subsequent to the opening of the new hospital rose rapidly. In 1786, the last year of the "Foundry" hospital, there were 106 at the time of the annual report. The numbers hereafter rose in the immediately following years to 119, 170, 183, 218, 221, 228 and the house expenses rose correspondingly from £2,199 to £2,585, £2,661, £3,585, £3,556, £4,096, £4,226.

It should be remembered that for the uncured who were re-admitted a sum of five shillings a week was paid by their parishes, relations or friends, and that a part, therefore, of the house expenses was met by these fees.

The servants and attendants had, as already mentioned, asked for and been refused a rise in their wages, but in 1789 all "acknowledgments" and wages were reconsidered and the following scale, which also gives their duties, was approved by the Courts:

Physician	£100
Surgeon	£ 50
Secretary	£100 without gratuity
Apothecary	£ 60 instead of £ 40
Master	£ 60 ,, ,, £ 40

33

Matron.	£ 40 instead of £ 30	
Matron's Assistant . . .	£ 25 ,, ,, £ 20	
Porter, the 3 Man Keepers and the Provision Carver . .	£ 20 ,, ,, £ 14	
Cook		
4 Gallery Maids . . .	£ 16 ,, ,, £ 12	
2 Laundry Maids . . .		
2 House Maids . . .		

Despite the cost of the new hospital, the "clear estate" or what would now be called the assets of the Charity, had been well maintained, thanks to the careful management of the Treasurer and General Committee and to generous donations from the public. For example, the clear estate of St. Luke's in 1782 before a penny had been spent on the new hospital was about £95,000, and in 1792, after the hospital was finished, it was nearly £100,000, not including the building which was insured at considerably less than its true value for £20,000. Space does not allow a list of benefactors, but donations of £1,000 were not uncommon, and in 1793 an anonymous donor gave through Messrs. Charles & Robert Drummond, the bankers, a sum of £10,000 to be divided equally between Bethlem and St. Luke's.

In this year the Committee were faced with a problem which may have been common enough in those days, but which was unique as far as the Hospital was concerned. At their meeting in October the Secretary reported that an estate in Dominica on which, among others, an annuity of £50 was secured to the Charity, was not producing enough to pay the total amount of the annuities, namely £600. It was proposed, therefore, to sell the slaves on the estate. The Court authorised the Treasurer to accept the proposal, but the subsequent negotiations dragged on several years, and seem to have ended by the annuitants losing most of their money.

During the second half of the eighteenth century the diet of the patients was unchanged except that occasionally they were allowed veal or pork as a change from their perpetual beef or mutton. The Committee continued to exercise care when accepting a contract and more than once refused to approve the lowest tender because they thought the provisions would not be up to the standard they demanded. The price of meat rose steadily from about 2s. 6d. per stone in 1787 to over 5s. in 1801, but it fell to 4s. 7d. in 1803.

Bread was also a problem in those years of war with Napoleon. In 1796 the Committee and Dr. Simmons met to consider the recommendation of Parliament that bread should be of mixed wheat and barley flour and resolved that, during the scarcity of wheat, the bread for the patients should be two thirds wheat and one third barley. Accordingly they accepted a contract of 4½d. the half peck under the assize price, and they also suggested to the House Committee that rice should be tried. Dr. Simmons, however, reported, after a short trial, that such bread disagreed with the patients and that he (and the patients) would not even agree to a mixture of which one quarter should be barley flour. Rice does not seem to have been tried. The English of the eighteenth century, even when paupers and not quite right in the head, complained that they could not stomach any but good wheaten bread, and they got it. On more than one occasion the baker was cautioned for supplying bread that was not up to the quality required. On the whole, the patients of St. Luke's were fortunate during the Napoleonic Wars.

It was at this time that the Committee decided to erect their own oven and bake their own bread. In April 1796 that remarkable and ingenious American, Count Rumford, better known as Sir Benjamin Thompson, the Founder of the Royal Institution, came to their meeting to advise them as to what would be the best position for the oven. This he did, and offered to send them a plan of an oven which he was erecting in the Foundling Hospital. However, there was no further mention of him or his oven in the Minutes.

During these lean years it continued to be impossible to make any contract for butter or cheese, and the Committee arranged for a supply on the most favourable terms possible in the market. Small beer also rose in price owing to the additional duty on malt, first to 16s. and later to 19s. a barrel.

The number of patients continued to increase, and after 1797 was rarely below 300, the normal proportion being about 180 curable and 120 incurable patients, and the over-all cost of feeding them was about £14 8s. per head per annum.

From 1801 onwards the accounts were set out in a different form, and far more clearly. In 1803 the income and expenditure were given by the auditors as follows:

INCOME

	£	s.	d.
Cash in hand	27	17	9
Legacies	1,081	14	7
Board of uncured patients . . .	445	0	0
Revenue from the General Fund . .	5,571	6	0
	£7,125	18	4

EXPENDITURE

	£	s.	d.
Salaries	531	0	0
Wages	280	3	0
Rent and Taxes	243	13	8
Medicines	84	19	0
Repairs	74	1	6
House expenses	5,288	1	3
Law Charges	43	15	0
Stationery	91	16	0
Subscriptions	10	10	0
Balance	477	18	11
	£7,125	18	4

Looking back, the writing on the wall is clear; costs of every kind were rising, and it might have been prudent to restrict expenditure to the income received from the General Fund plus the fees on account of uncured patients, and to have invested the bulk of the legacies, thus gradually to increase the General Fund and its income, and to have admitted patients accordingly; but it is always easy to be wise after the event, and there was every reason for the Governors to be optimistic, for their Balance Sheet was a strong one, the assets consisting as they did of:

	£	s.	d.
1. The Building insured for . . .	20,000	0	0
2. Funds with a book value of . .	137,000	0	0
3. Legacies due to the Hospital . .	7,975	0	0
4. Annual Subscriptions . . .	110	5	0

Dr. William Rawes in his *History of St. Luke's*, dated 1904, when he was Medical Superintendent of the hospital, wrote:

"In order the better to be able to appreciate the changes that have taken place during the last century, let us pay a visit to the Hospital in October 1803, and get Mr. Dunston to show us over it. The wards are shut off from the central portion by thick upright iron bars and heavy iron gates which afford a complete view of their whole length on each side. The south side of each ward contains seventeen single bedrooms, ventilated by grills above the doors, and lighted by small, half-moon-shaped windows containing four panes of glass not much larger than a man's hand, so that scarcely a ray of sunlight can penetrate. Besides single rooms of a like kind, there are eight large windows on the north side capable of being opened at the top, but strongly guarded by thick wire netting, through which can be seen on the male side the parish burial ground, with perhaps a funeral taking place. The females are better off, as opposite their gallery is a recreation ground used for playing bowls, and a large fish-pond, patronised by boys and youths in summer as a bathing place.

"The wards open directly into the wings, so that a classi-fication of patients was not possible on any floor. There is no furniture beyond bare tables and wooden forms. The walls are not even white-washed. There are no fire-places or any means whatever of heating the wards. Padded rooms are unknown. There are no infirmaries or places where sick patients can be treated apart from the others. There is a large cold-water bath in the basement on each side, into which the patients are thrown when occasion requires, but facilities for a warm bath do not exist.

"In the wings are rooms capable of containing four patients each, besides several single rooms. Each patient has a wooden trough-shaped bedstead fixed into the wall, and containing loose straw, which is covered with rough sacking in the cases of convalescing patients only. There are nearly three hundred patients in residence, two thirds being acute cases. The incurable patients are kept in the basement, many of them chained to the wall, though allowed a fair latitude of movement. All have loose straw to sleep on, but no bedsteads. The noisy acute cases are in seclusion; those who are violent are chained to their bedsteads, covered only with a loose rug, or in the case of females with a loose blanket gown."

The foregoing description of the hospital is sadly inadequate and most difficult to understand. Moreover, although the exterior is today unchanged as the St. Luke's Printing Works of the Bank of England, the whole interior was gutted by the Bank in order to make the floors strong enough to bear heavy machinery and the accommodation necessary for modern offices and stores. Consequently, a visit to the works is of no help in visualising the original hospital, and no plans exist of Mr. Dance's building; therefore it is possible only to gather what it was like from the account of alterations carried out in subsequent years as recorded in the Minutes.

Dr. Rawes gave an interesting account of the views of Mr. Dunston about the treatment of insanity at this period. He did not unfortunately give his authority for these opinions. Mr. Dunston must, of course, have been dead long before Dr. Rawes wrote his history, and there are no papers, printed or otherwise, in the archives of the hospital which confirm them. It is possible, however, that, when the Old Street Hospital was sold in 1916, some records may unhappily have been lost.

It is almost certain, however, that a physician of the standing and reputation of Dr. Rawes had good authority for categorically stating the opinions of Mr. Dunston on so vital a matter, and these are of importance in view of the reputation of the hospital and its Master, for at that time and for many years afterwards St. Luke's was looked upon as one of the best-managed institutions of its kind in Europe.

Dr. Rawes wrote that the patients in 1803 escaped being bled and purged every spring and autumn as was done in other hospitals. The medical treatment at St. Luke's consisted principally in the use of anti-spasmodics, emetics and purgatives, and in the Minutes it was occasionally recorded that Dr. Simmons finding that a patient was in "too weak a state of health to take medicines proper for their lunacy", the Committee gave orders that his or her securities be written to take them away.

Mr. Dunston, however, is quoted by Dr. Rawes as having no great faith in medicinal treatment. He relied chiefly on management, and he alone (apart from the medical staff) had the power of ordering seclusion for or putting manacles on patients in case of violence or as a punishment. What he believed to be most effectual with the insane was their fear, and particularly their fear of punishment. Presumably, therefore, these forms of restraint were employed rather as an example than as a regular form of treatment, and although St. Luke's had not fully followed the example of Pinel in France in 1792 or Tuke at the Retreat in York, opened in 1796, there was less restraint and that of a less barbarous nature than obtained elsewhere. Mr. Dunston considered that the strait-waistcoat should be used as little as possible, "for it was heating, it confined the upper arms, was not pleasant to the patient and was hurtful to the joints". On the other hand he believed in the chain because the very idea of it gave the patients the impression that they were confined while actually it gave them more liberty and did not stop the circulation of the blood. Patients who were wet and dirty were kept in bed for one day while their clothes were washed, after which they were allowed to walk about again (presumably still wearing their light chains). There were strict orders that every patient sleeping in an associated room, i.e., a room in which there were more than one patient, was safely chained before the attendants went off duty. Such precautions were thought necessary at a time when the proportion of attendants to patients was so small, and there were no attendants on night duty.

Dr. Gardiner Hill, many years later before his appointment to the Lincoln Asylum in 1835, visited Bethlem where he said "all kinds of instruments were in use and some of the patients were chained to the seats in the airing courts. . . . Many were very ferocious, the hubbub and noise being almost deafening. At St. Luke's Hospital the same state of things existed. At that asylum I was shown a bath of surprise." Allowing for possible exaggeration on the part of one who wrote to prove that he was largely responsible for the abolition of restraint in English asylums, it would seem that conditions were not as lenient as Dr. Rawes and Mr. Dunston made out.

Despite such treatment, out of a total of 7,488 who had been admitted between 1751, when St. Luke's was opened, and 1803, nearly 44 per cent. had been discharged cured. Doubtless, the physicians and surgeons were among the most eminent who then treated this tragic form of illness, but apart from their previous experience at Bethlem and elsewhere, neither the Mansfields nor the Dunstons had or could have had any scientific knowledge about lunacy, for this literally did not exist at this period. Obviously therefore any examination for them or for the attendants was out of the question. All that some of them may have had was experience or what they had learned from the medical officers of the hospital.

This period when restraint was practised in some more or less modified form, severity depending on individual physicians and hospital "masters", continued until about 1837.

IV

THE BEGINNING OF REFORMS IN TREATMENT

IN the early years of the nineteenth century, public opinion, lay as well as medical, must have been deeply concerned by the illness, recovery and final complete relapse of the King. Wynn's Act for the better care and maintenance of lunatics and the establishment of county asylums, first passed in 1808 and renewed and amended in 1811, 1815, 1819 and 1824, was an indication that the public and political conscience had been more than pricked by the royal tragedy.

But there were other factors and influences at work tending to improve the lot of lunatics. The "Retreat" established near York in 1791 by the Society of Friends was founded largely in protest against the hideous abuses and cruelties in the York Asylum as disclosed by a determined and courageous magistrate, and the treatment there set an example of milder and more humane methods with little or no restraint. There had, also, been Committees of Enquiry in Parliament and these had discovered abuses in the treatment of lunatics all over the country including Bethlem Hospital. No one can read the journals of those days without being struck by the number of articles on the subject of lunacy; the *Quarterly Review*, for instance, contained many articles in its earliest numbers dealing with some aspect of the subject. In these articles St. Luke's Hospital was held to be in a more satisfactory condition than Bethlem but the general treatment was similar. Chains and fetters were employed and there was then no attempt at classification. The Governors must have known of the general feeling that the treatment of the insane was very far from what it should be in the country generally, and it is possible occasionally to read between the lines of the formally, almost primly, worded Minutes of those days and to discern here and there a conflict between those who wished for more progressive treatment and those whose loyalty to the Hospital induced the not uncommon attitude that "what was good enough for our fathers is good enough for us, and why should we have visitors from outside when we choose the best medical staff we can find and ourselves inspect the hospital frequently". This resulted time and again in the record that "further consideration was deferred" to the next and sometimes many succeeding meetings of the Committee.

So long as Dr. Simmons was Physician to the hospital, it was unlikely that there would have been any marked change in the treatment of the patients. George III was entrusted to his care in 1803 and he was again in attendance in 1811 when the King became permanently insane. He seems to have been a believer in severe treatment; that is, if the stories are true of the occasional roughness with which the unfortunate Monarch was treated. Under his guidance, restraint, even though it may have been mild compared to what was practised elsewhere, was continued at St. Luke's. On his retirement in 1811 the General Court showed their appreciation of his 30 years of service by electing him a Life Governor and appointing him consulting physician.

At a court where no less than 177 Governors were present, Dr. A. R. Sutherland was elected to succeed him. For 18 years he was the sole physician, and for 12 more he acted jointly with Dr. John Warburton, who was appointed in 1829 when the Governors decided that there should be a second physician.

There seems to have been a gradual reduction in restraint at St. Luke's after 1811, but it was not until 1828 that the number of patients under restraint was reported at each weekly meeting of the House Committee by the resident apothecary. In that year the average number was about 28 out of 245 patients. As late as 1840 Drs. Sutherland and Warburton in their annual report wrote:

"The entire exclusion of restraint in the treatment of insanity has recently been spoken of and said to have been actually carried into effect, which can only be conceived as applying to a class of chronic cases, when the disease has quieted down into a state of harmless fatuity as exemplified in St. Luke's among the class of incurables. In the incipient and active stages of many forms of mental disease, judicious and considerable restraint is not only called for as a salutary process, but cannot be dispensed with as a protection to the afflicted individual, not only against himself but others. Medical and moral treatment may effect much in assuaging and subduing maniacal action, but much is yet to be arrived at before such can be relied upon as a substitute for personal restraint, the total and indiscriminate abandonment of which in all cases of insanity must be considered fallacious, experimental and hazardous, to which an awful responsibility would attach."

It is evident that the writers did not agree with Drs. Pinel, Tuke or Gardiner Hill. Possibly they may have read—and resented—the latter's remarks on his visit to St. Luke's, but it should be remembered that, at this period, the very nature of insanity as well as the best means of treating it were still matters of controversy among the leading authorities. In any case, it is clear that, until there came a younger generation of medical officers and superintendents, some form of restraint would be continued at the hospital.

It must not, however, be supposed that, because these senior and experienced men reported thus adversely on the removal of restraint, they did not do valuable and progressive work at St. Luke's. In 1829 the first of the Physicians' annual reports was entered in the Minutes of the General Court. In 1829 and 1830 they were signed by Dr. Sutherland alone and thereafter by both doctors, who consistently recommended a more complete separation of the different categories of patients and also that there should be a limit to the numbers admitted so that accommodation could be re-arranged and patients more exactly classified. Soon after the appointment of Dr. Warburton they suggested an entirely fresh distribution in the galleries, their plan being based on the fact that the number of female patients was always greater than of males. Their scheme allowed for the accommodation of 90 curable and 59 incurable females, and 74 curable and 53 incurable male patients, a total of 276, which in fact was greater than the actual number of patients admitted. This arrangement facilitated a much more exact classification, to which they attached considerable importance.

They also recommended that patients should be allowed to go from the hospital "on leave", or perhaps it would be more accurate to say "on trial". This in Dr. Sutherland's opinion would enable the list of "uncured" to be reduced and the returns called for by the Lord Chancellor to present a more favourable appearance and compare more exactly with those from Bethlem. It was during this period and on the recommendation of the physicians that hot baths for the patients were constructed. The Committee in the first instance suggested a movable "slipper bath", but this form of economy was overruled.

The reports of the physicians always showed anxiety for the improvement of the hospital and a desire to carry out the intention of the founders, that is to say to help that "middle class of society" not rich enough to send their relations to private institutions and too proud to allow them to be classed as "parish poor".

The cholera epidemic of 1832-33 led to consideration of infirmary accommodation for those who, apart from their mental state, were sick and needed special attention. In the first instance an infirmary was built in the grounds of the hospital, but this was not found satisfactory or convenient and two rooms in the attic storey were converted for this purpose. In later years the original infirmary became the Hospital Chapel.

From 1833 onwards the physicians urged the Committee to promote and encourage occupation and amusement for the patients. At this time they did not say that this was a necessity; they preferred to leave it open to individual benevolence, by which means "£15 has already been raised as a Library Fund". This was the first mention in the Minutes of some form of occupational therapy, not then recognised as part of the medical treatment, but regarded as an "extra" to be provided by charity, and this despite the fact that, owing to the growth of London, St. Luke's became yearly more and more shut in by dreary and depressing surroundings, necessitating some form of occupation and interest inside the hospital to help recovery and prevent melancholia. Gradually, however, the value and necessity of this form of therapy were realised. In 1842 the "Cambridge Fund"—so named in honour of the President— was instituted to provide occupation for male patients. For the women it had hitherto been assumed that they would find amusement as well as occupation in the laundry. (In 1825, a lady governor had suggested a Ladies' Committee, but the General Committee on the advice of Dr. Sutherland did not approve the idea. Had there been such a Committee the views of the Governors regarding the amusement of female patients might have been revised.)

However, by 1842 there were reading rooms for both sexes, a piano for dancing, bagatelle tables, cards, draughts, trap-ball and "Les Graces", whatever that may have been.

On the whole the standard of the attendants was rising steadily and a number of them qualified for special grants and higher wages by their long and faithful service. In 1809 Mr. Dunston had reported that, in consequence of the low wages given to the servants, he found it very difficult to get "proper persons to do the service of the house". The Committee consequently raised the men's yearly wages from £21 to £25 and the women's from £18 to £20. All servants must have benefited from training by Mr. Dunston who had had a very long, possibly too long, experience in the care of the insane. Among the female staff, now all called nurses, Rebecca Cochran deserves particular mention. She was given a special annual pension of £25 when, for reasons of health, and being over 70 years of age, she retired, having been upwards of 40 years in the laundry.

The general good conduct and, in some recorded instances, self-sacrificing and patient behaviour under provocation, of the great majority of the staff must be offset against the few occasions when justified complaints were made about them. As an instance of the risk involved it may be mentioned that in 1814, one of the male attendants had received such injuries from a patient that the Committee sent him into the country to recuperate and gave him a special grant of £10.

On the other hand in 1817 Mr. George D'Aranda, apothecary since 1814, resigned as he considered that he was no longer supported by the Governors. He made a general accusation that the officers and servants knocked the patients about "like beasts in Smithfield". At an extraordinary Meeting called at the request of the staff, the General Committee investigated these charges and came to the conclusion that they were wholly unfounded, but they added that the charges were "of so grave and serious a nature and replete with matter so injurious to the credit of the hospital" that they requested the

General Court to give the matter their special consideration. The Court, having examined the evidence, confirmed the conclusion of the Committee.

In 1827, a patient, who had been discharged uncured, in a letter to the Lord Chancellor complained of the treatment and the food in the hospital, and of the fact that there was no medical officer on duty at night. The Lord Chancellor ordered an enquiry to be made by two expert and specially appointed physicians. They reported that this gentleman, although quite coherent, was undoubtedly insane and suffered from persecution mania. They considered that his health did not seem to have suffered from his confinement nor did his appearance show any want of nourishment. The food, in their opinion, was more liberal in quantity than full diet in other hospitals, and of good quality, though "perhaps different from that to which a person in his former station in life was accustomed". As regards management and treatment, the investigators reported that the House Committee met weekly and went round the wards afterwards and had therefore full opportunities of hearing complaints; the medical treatment they considered satisfactory but they criticised the permission that had been given recently to the Apothecary to sleep out of the hospital. This was the first recorded official inspection of the hospital from the outside, and the findings are, therefore, given in some detail although the accusations need not be treated seriously as the complainant was incurably mad.

The permission given to the Apothecary to sleep away from the hospital was withdrawn and not long after a nightly watch was instituted. Despite this, however, a patient was killed in 1831. He was in a room with others and although there was a standing order that in such rooms all patients should be chained to their beds when the attendants went off duty, this was neglected, and during the night the unfortunate man was beaten to death by the other patients, and the nightly watch had heard nothing. For their neglect to chain up the patients two male Keepers were discharged.

In 1832-33 the case of a discharged patient who said he had been beaten was taken up by a friend, Mr. Wakefield. At a preliminary examination the Committee considered that cruelty was not proved; but the friend was persistent and the complaint renewed. Further examination convinced the

Committee that the patient had been ill-treated by two Keepers, of whom one had been already discharged, and the other had left at his own request. A resolution was passed to the effect that the Committee were "greatly grieved to find that such conduct should have existed and that the resident officers should have been ignorant of it". The Apothecary and Superintendent were both admonished. This, however, did not save the Committee from a very severe letter from Mr. Wakefield. They seem indeed to have treated him with scant and formal courtesy, for they merely acknowledged his letters and gave him no thanks for having drawn their attention to a very unsatisfactory and indeed scandalous business. Such isolated incidents must be compared with the mention repeated year after year in the Physicians' reports of the gratitude expressed by discharged patients for the care and treatment they had received while in St. Luke's. An example of such gratitude was a letter quoted in the Minutes of the House Committee from a working man enclosing £10 to testify a deep sense of his obligation . . . "for the kind attention to his daughter during her trying affliction, and humbly begging the Committee's acceptance of his mite towards the support of their praiseworthy institution".

The exact daily diet was not given in the Minutes of the House Committee until 1829. For some years previously the only food contract quoted had been for meat. For this, prices ranged from 6s. 4d. in 1814 to 3s. 2d. in 1821 for a stone of 8 lb. In 1829 or 1830 the patients began to get milk at 1s. 3d. a gallon and in 1834 a bill for "groceries, tea and rice" was mentioned for the first time.

In the year 1829, the "ordinary", "milk", "low" and "broth" diets are shown as under in the House Committee Minutes:

ORDINARY DIET

BREAKFAST

Males: 2 pints of gruel[1] made of milk and water and 2 oz. bread.

Females: 1½ pints gruel.

---

[1] We do not know whether the gruel Mr. Wodehouse preferred was of the same description.

DINNER

Males: ¾ lb. meat, with vegetables and 6 oz. bread.
Females: ½ lb. meat, with vegetables and bread.
> *or*

Broth: meat with peas (16 lb. meat for 50 patients), 2 or 1½ pints with 6 oz. bread.
> *or*

1 or ¾ pint broth, 4 oz. bread, ¾ or ½ lb. baked suet pudding.
> *or*

2 or 1½ lb. rice milk.
> *or*

1 or ¾ lb. baked rice pudding.

SUPPER

8 oz. bread, 2 oz. cheese or butter.

MILK DIET

BREAKFAST
1 or ¾ pint milk porridge.

DINNER
2 or 1½ pints milk with arrowroot or sago, 6 oz. bread.

SUPPER
1 pint barley water, 8 or 6 oz. bread.

NO BEER

LOW DIET

BREAKFAST
¾ or ½ pint milk porridge.

DINNER
1 pint milk with arrowroot, 6 oz. bread.

SUPPER
1 pint barley water, 6 oz. bread.

BROTH DIET

BREAKFAST
¾ or ½ pint milk porridge.

DINNER
2 pints broth, 6 oz. bread, 1 pint beer.

SUPPER
6 oz. bread, 1 oz. cheese or butter, beer.

Apparently patients received a small quantity of vegetables though they are not included amongst the bills. Presumably what they received was grown in the very small kitchen garden within the hospital walls, and potatoes were not included.

At this time butter averaged about 1s. a lb. and cheese about 6d. Bacon cost 5½d. a lb.

Although the diet may have lacked some of the vitamins considered desirable, if not essential, today, it was certainly liberal. Unfortunately the numbers of patients on the different diets are not given.

The Resident Officers and servants were also well fed. In 1836 the meat supplied to them was as follows:

Mondays:	Buttock of beef, occasionally a steak or mutton chop.
Tuesdays:	Roast mutton.
Wednesdays:	Boiled mutton or pickled pork.
Thursdays:	The same as on Mondays.
Fridays:	The same as on Tuesdays.
Saturdays:	*Servants*—Thick flank or beef for pies.
Saturdays:	*Officers*—Steak or chump of veal.
Sundays:	Roasting beef or fillet or shoulder of veal.

For 28 persons the daily allowance was 35 or 40 lb. of meat, and presumably the ration of bread and butter or cheese was at least as liberal as that of the patients. Here again there is no mention of potatoes or vegetables.

As regards personnel, the list of those who held office during these years is contained in Appendix I. It is, however, worthy of note that John Clark Powell succeeded his father as Treasurer of the Charity in 1810 and that the total length of time during which these two guided the policy and guarded the finances of St. Luke's when John Powell retired in 1843 was only one year short of a half century. In 1839 the General Committee met specially at St. Luke's, having been requested by the House Committee to see the portrait of Mr. Powell painted by Mr. John Irvine, a patient, who received 45 guineas subscribed by the gentlemen of the Committee and the Physicians.

In 1830 Thomas Dunston died in the hospital. He had been

in the service of the Governors since 1781 when he and his wife came from Bethlem as Master and Matron. When Mrs. Dunston died in 1816 he had wished to retire, but the Governors persuaded him to remain on as Superintendent, and he spent 49 years at St. Luke's.

In the 1830 list of 277 Governors is included the name of Charles Lamb, Esq., of Enfield. His sister had been temporarily insane in tragic circumstances but was not a patient in St. Luke's. Among his published letters is one dated the 8th March, 1830, in which he wrote:

> "I was over St. Luke's the other day with my friend Tuthill[1] and mightily pleased with one of his contrivances for the comfort and amelioration of the students [*sic*]. They have double cells in which a pair may lie feet to feet horizontally, and chat the time away as rationally as they can. It must certainly be more sociable for them these warm raving nights."

Another letter was from Mrs. Elizabeth Fry[2] to the Matron of St. Luke's Hospital and preserved in the Visitors' Book.

> "E. Fry wishes C. Stinton to make
> any use she pleases of this letter.
>
> > "54, Devonshire Street,
> > Portland Place.
> > 4th month 7: 1831.
>
> "It is I think three or four years since I last visited the female side of St. Luke's Hospital and I am glad to be able to state that as far as I could observe there appeared to be a material improvement in the state of the institution, particularly in the comfort of the Patients and in their general accommodation. They seemed to be under *much* less restraint and I should think from what I heard and saw, that

---

[1] Sir George L. Tuthill, M.D., also a Governor and an occasional witness in Lunacy cases.

[2] Elizabeth Fry, 1780-1845. A member of the old Quaker family of Gurney who married Joseph Fry in 1800. She was a devoted and lifelong prison reformer and had an immense reputation, not only in the United Kingdom, but in Europe. She was also the friend and benefactor of all homeless wanderers and unemployed persons and, as this letter shows, of the insane.

there is more kindness shown them. The Galleries, I thought cold, so much so, that I should fear in winter the delicate Patients must suffer a good deal. The bedding, I thought good, and the arrangements excellent for the dirty patients, with the exception of their having no garment on, a deficiency which I could not but regret, as there is not only a want of propriety in it, as it respects even their Attendants, but the straw must irritate the skin, and I am of the opinion that if a Patient should be so ungovernable that no garment *can* be worn, the straw should be put into a cover. I think advantage would result from a greater variety of books of rather an amusing nature, such as Kildare Street Library and costs only 8/- per dozen; it is very important to have the mind properly occupied and the attention engaged as far as it can be. I observed there is not much employment, and I would recommend, if possible, the introduction of some, as it surely tends to the happiness of the Patients and often to their recovery. In many institutions of a similar nature there is now religious service and its results have frequently been very favourable, but I am sensible that much judgment and prudence are required in the conduct of it, and therefore great caution should be used as to the manner in which it is established.

"My Sister Buxton accompanied me in my visit, and fully united with me in the observations which I have made. I cannot conclude without expressing how much we were pleased with the kind and judicious treatment of the lunatics, also as far as we could judge, with the attention paid them by the Nurses.

"I remain,

thy friend,

(signed) E. Fry."

One wishes that there had been more visitors capable of writing such illuminating and charming letters.

Among other miscellaneous items of information recorded in the Minutes was a Memorial from Bethlem Hospital in 1809, asking that in the "Considerations upon the usefulness and necessity of establishing an Hospital . . . for poor lunatics, etc." it was still stated as in the original paper that Bethlem was incapable of receiving and providing for all the patients

51

who applied for admission, that it was both difficult and expensive to get into that hospital and that consequently fatal acts of violence resulted, committed by potentially useful members of society.

The Committee of Bethlem left it to the Governors of St. Luke's to amend the above paper accordingly, and the General Committee thereon resolved that all mention of Bethlem should be omitted in this paper and that the following words should be substituted "that no particular provision had at that time been made by law for lunatics" and that "parish workhouses were noways proper for their reception".

In 1803 the resident staff of the hospital were: The Master and Matron, the Apothecary, 10 maids and 6 men for 275 patients. By 1842 the staff for 210 patients had grown and now consisted of the Steward and Matron, the Apothecary-Surgeon, 15 nurses and 10 male attendants. Among the male attendants was the Porter who, in 1808 had been provided with a proper gown and a laced hat.

In 1843 the Committee passed a resolution to the effect that the income tax paid by the Steward, the Matron and the Apothecary should be refunded to them. Fortunately for the finances of St. Luke's, this did not amount to the sum that it would have cost in 1948.

In 1809 the Court of the Bank of England decided to pay the Charity 20 guineas annually and it was thereupon agreed that the Governor and Court should be admitted to all the privileges of Governors of St. Luke's.

In 1826 gas was laid into the hospital "for the purpose of lighting the galleries instead of the portable gas at present used". This was one of the many improvements in the building. The interior had been whitewashed or painted at regular intervals and there had been additional single rooms. Water closets had been made and airing grounds had been increased and made more comfortable. But in the time of Mr. Dunston security was still regarded as being of prime importance and it was he who had urged that iron bars should be fitted in the galleries and windows.

Mrs. Fry was not the first nor the last to complain of the coldness of the building. For many years the attention of the Committee had been drawn to this, but in those days neither the ventilation nor the heating of large buildings was efficient.

Large open fires with smoke and heat pouring up the chimneys were the usual means adopted, and these were built in each of the galleries in 1842. St. Luke's, however, must have presented particular difficulties owing to draughts caused by long open galleries and a number of unglazed interior windows. In 1856 the Governors employed a self-styled expert and spent much money on stoves and iron flues, only to discover that the latter were so faultily designed that the result would have been that the whole building would probably have been set on fire. So the work had to be done again, this time under the supervision of an expert surveyor and architect.

In 1831 a special report was printed and circulated to the Governors and public. The Committee recapitulated the history of the hospital and described their ever-increasing expenses with a view to encouraging donations and subscriptions. They pointed out that originally no payment was asked on the admission of patients from "the middle order of the people", but that after a few years it had been decided to re-admit a few of their own incurables at 5s. a week.

Subsequently unavoidable causes, such as the late war, the high cost of provisions and the increased number of patients, had necessitated a departure from the intentions of the founders and made it necessary to ask for a payment on admission of £3 from patients of the middle class, of £6 for parish patients and 7s. a week from incurables.

Realising that these fees were such a departure, the Committee had not "been wanting in their endeavours to restore to the patients the full benefits they once possessed; and they are happy to inform the Governors that notwithstanding the causes above mentioned, and the great and necessarily expensive improvements, they have been able to reduce the admission fees from £3 to £1, from £6 to £4, and the weekly payments for incurables from 7s. to 6s., and hope with the assistance of a generous public to do away with admission fees altogether and to reduce the charge for incurables to the original 5s. a week, and they respectfully appeal to the Governors and the public for their co-operation and support".

This rather optimistic report went on to mention the appointment of a second physician in order to give the patients more frequent medical visits.

It was realised that there had been great improvements in the design of asylums since St. Luke's had been built and the Committee, being anxious to make the hospital as good as possible, had asked the physicians to suggest how the building could be improved. The suggestions included alterations to galleries, sleeping and sitting rooms in order to facilitate the classification of patients, which had hitherto been impossible. Warm baths had been fitted on both sides of the hospital; windows of improved design had been fitted to the small rooms and the airing grounds for both sexes had been made more comfortable. Interior communications had been established and a night watch was kept throughout the hospital.

The paper concluded by emphasising that these changes had been most expensive and a heavy charge on the funds of the Charity.

Although addressed primarily to the Governors, this was in effect the first public appeal by the Committee—80 years after the opening of the hospital. It was becoming evident that everything required by a hospital was going to cost more and more and that the luxuries of the past would become necessities. The industrial age had begun, and though life and conditions in most factories were grim beyond description, the general standard of life was rising. It was also an age of humanitarianism. Elizabeth Fry and Lord Ashley, afterwards Earl of Shaftesbury, were only two among many interested in such establishments as St. Luke's. The following pages will tell something of its inspections and consequent criticism. By 1842 they had not begun, although there were signs of the public interest in such questions.

In 1837 the Governors applied for an Act of Incorporation; this received the Royal Assent in July 1838, at a cost to the Charity of £400 18s. 0d. Consequent on this, a seal was designed for St. Luke's by Mr. Wyon of the Mint. This cost 15 guineas and the press, which was in use up to 1948, cost the same. The seal was and is kept in a metal case with three locks, of which the keys were kept by the Treasurer, one of the Vice-Presidents and the Secretary. It was also decided at this time that the Funds of the hospital should be invested on behalf of the President, Vice-Presidents, Treasurer and Governors of St. Luke's or in the names of the Trustees. Gradually, as the Trustees died off, all funds were invested for the President, etc. It was then officially resolved that all funds should be invested in Parliamentary Stocks or Public Funds, or Mortgage of hereditaments in England or Wales.

The President, the Duke of Leeds, who had succeeded his father in this office, died in 1838. The Earl of Clarendon, the senior Vice-President, was elected President, but died the following year, and H.R.H. the Duke of Cambridge was elected President in February 1849, and in March of that year showed his interest in the hospital by presiding at a General Committee Meeting.

In 1841, Dr. A. R. Sutherland resigned, and was succeeded by his son, Dr. A. J. Sutherland, and in 1842, Dr. John Warburton was succeeded by Dr. Francis Richard Philp. Under the new physicians reforms and improvements were soon pressed on the Committee.

Already they had been asked to repeal that rule previously mentioned, that in rooms where more than one patient slept they were to be locked to their beds by keepers and nurses before they went off duty. This rule, according to the physicians, took from them the responsibility for ordering restraint. It was bad for those who were dirty but harmless. Such patients should be allowed freedom at night. The physicians ended by stating definitely that they could not reduce restraint so long as this rule was enforced.

After the appointment of Dr. Philp, the physicians became still more insistent. In December 1842 they reminded the Committee that by the Act passed during the previous year St. Luke's had become liable to be visited by two Metropolitan Commissioners instructed to report to the Lord Chancellor the state and condition of the hospital, the system of treatment, whether any system of non-coercion had been adopted wholly or partially, on the classification of patients and on their occupation and amusement.

The physicians regretted that funds did not allow of arrangements for complete classification, or for warming the galleries (which had been approved in principle a year previously) or for the appointment of a Chaplain and the fitting up of a chapel. They were anxious to carry out a system of non-coercion. They recommended that dirty and noisy patients should be accommodated on the ground floor and separated from one another and that patients generally should be classed not as curable or incurable but as noisy, dirty, or convalescent. They considered that five-bedded rooms were undesirable and should be divided by partitions. Though they admitted that many improvements had been carried out in recent years, they thought that there still were some urgent ones. For instance, the iron gates at the ends of the galleries should be abolished as they produced a prison-like and depressing effect; padded rooms should be fitted and special airing courts should be arranged so that the violent patients could get exercise.

This report and the likelihood of the Commissioners' impending visits produced what may perhaps be described as "inspection fever" among the Committee. A special Sub-Committee was at once appointed and in a few weeks their recommendations which endorsed those of the physicians were put in hand. They included the appointment of two more nurses for the laundry so that female patients in larger numbers could be employed there.

Thus the year 1842 ended with steps taken to modernise the hospital which it should be remembered had, in spite of some defects, done much to improve the unhappy lot of poor lunatics during its 90 years of existence.

During the years 1803-1842 the revenue from invested funds had not varied much; in 1803 it was £4,572 and in 1842 £4,804. Salaries and wages had doubled from £811 to £1,730. House expenses varied considerably; in 1803 they were shown as £5,289, and they rose to over £6,000 in the years 1810 to 1814, and fell after Waterloo to about £5,200 till 1821; there was a further fall and from 1822 they averaged £4,227.

The total amount spent on repairs, maintenance and new construction during the period was £21,200 and of this more than £9,100 was expended in the years 1833-42.

V

CENTENARY OF ST. LUKE'S. CHARLES DICKENS' VISIT. INSPECTION FROM OUTSIDE

ST. LUKE'S was not affected by any Lunacy Acts until 1842. In 1774 the first of these Acts was passed and by it private asylums were licensed and became liable to visitation. It proved, however, quite inadequate and did not prevent gross and horrible abuses. In 1828 it was repealed. By a new Act (9 Geo. IV. C.41) nearly all asylums were made liable to visitation. There were various groups of Commissioners including the London Commissioners appointed by the Home Secretary, who, with the Lord Chancellor and the Lords Justices, became more or less jointly responsible for the administration of asylums. In 1832 the London Commissioners became Metropolitan, responsible only to the Lord Chancellor. So far both Bethlem and St. Luke's had been independent and exempt from visitation, but by an Act passed in 1841 they became liable to visitation at first by the Metropolitan Commissioners and after 1845 by the Commissioners in Lunacy for all England and Wales.

The first years of visitation and criticism by governmental authorities were, as will be seen, expensive and probably trying for the Governors. Hitherto they had been a law unto themselves. They and their predecessors had, for 100 years, created and administered a great charitable institution, which had a deservedly high reputation with both the public and the medical profession, and there is no doubt that the Governors did not welcome with any enthusiasm the visitation of Commissioners appointed by and responsible to the Government. They "used all the means in their power" . . . to get the Charity exempted from the operation of the Act of 1845 for the Regulation of the Care and Treatment of Lunatics. This Act created a permanent Commission and authorised the visitation of all institutions and, in the words of the Minutes, placed St. Luke's "nearly under the same regulations as a private lunatic asylum". The Governors had always clung to the view of the founders that the hospital ought to be administered by its own patrons and supporters. Moreover, the Englishman of those days liked Government interference as little as he looked for Government help. However, the efforts of the Governors to get St. Luke's exempted were unsuccessful and they probably agreed with their chosen physicians when they wrote a few years later in one of their admirable reports that the hospital was "passing through one of those trials to which all Public Institutions in this country are subject": words that might indeed be applied to other periods in the history of English hospitals.

The Reports of the Commissioners were on the whole favourable and helpful although they were inclined to put forward counsels of perfection regardless of their cost in a fashion characteristic of some other social reformers.

But before dealing with these reports the centenary of the hospital in 1851 must be recorded. It was celebrated by a dinner presided over by the Rt. Hon. Charles Shaw Lefevre, Speaker of the House of Commons, at which over £2,000 was subscribed in aid of the Charity.

The Physicians presented an interesting report in the centenary year. In it they recapitulated the growth in the percentage of recoveries during the past thirty years, and the improvements made in the hospital during the previous ten years.

As, however, the report dealt mainly with the care and treatment of patients and recorded its development during the existence of St. Luke's Hospital, it is included in the Section dealing with nursing and treatment.

It can probably be accepted as the concise and considered opinion of the two physicians on the treatment of insanity so far as the conditions at St. Luke's Hospital and the state of medical knowledge then allowed. In subsequent reports they emphasised that St. Luke's was a hospital, and not an asylum and they implied that the Commissioners did not always recognise the distinction.

Another report which concerns the centenary celebrations, although not directly, was the description by Charles Dickens of his visit to St. Luke's on the night of Boxing Day in 1851. It was printed in *Household Words* of 1852, and is quoted both for its graphic description and because it tells something of the hospital from a purely human and unofficial point of view as opposed to the somewhat dry administrative records on which this history is otherwise dependent.

This account was reprinted by the Governors in 1883 with the author's permission together with a note on the changes introduced in the intervening thirty-one years.

"A CURIOUS DANCE ROUND A CURIOUS TREE"

"On the 13th day of January, 1750—when the corn that grew near Moorfields was ground on the top of Windmill Hill, 'Fensbury'; when Bethlehem Hospital was a 'dry walk for loiterers', and a show; when lunatics were chained, naked, in rows of cages that flanked a promenade, and were wondered and jeered at through iron bars by London loungers, half-a-dozen gentlemen met together to found a new Asylum for the Insane.

"With the benevolence which thus originated an additional mad-house, was mixed, as was usual in that age, a curious degree of unconscious cruelty. Coercion for the outward man, and rabid physicking for the inward man, were then the specifics for lunacy. Chains, straw, filthy solitude, darkness, and starvation; jalap, syrup of buckthorn, tartar-ised antimony, and ipecacuanha administered every spring and fall in fabulous doses to every patient, whether well or ill; spinning in whirligigs, corporal punishment, gagging, 'continued intoxication'; nothing was too widely extravagant, nothing too monstrously cruel, to be prescribed by mad-doctors. It was their monomania; and, under their influence, the directors of Lunatic Asylums acted. In other respects these Physicians were grave men, of mild dispositions, and— in their ample-flapped, ample-cuffed coats, with a certain gravity and air of state in the skirts; with their large buttons and gold-headed canes, their hair powder and ruffles—were men of benevolent aspects. Imagine one of them turning back his lace and tightening his wig to supply a maniac, who *would* keep his mouth shut, with food or physic. He employed a flat oval ring, with a handle to it. 'The head being placed between the knees of the operator, the patient blinded and properly secured, an opportunity is watched. When he opens his mouth to speak, the instrument is thrust in and allows the food or medicine to be introduced without difficulty. A

59

sternutatory of any kind' (say a pepper-castor of cayenne, or half an ounce of rappee) 'always forced the mouth open in spite of the patient's determination to keep it shut.' 'In cases of great fury and violence', says the amiable practitioner from whom I quote, 'the patient should be kept in a dark room, confined by one leg, with metallic manacles on the wrist; the skin being less liable to be injured',—here the good Doctor becomes especially considerate and mild—'the skin being less liable to be injured by the friction of polished metal than by that of linen or cotton.'

"The inside of the new Hospital, therefore, even when, in 1782, it was removed, under the name of 'St. Luke's', from Windmill Hill to its present site in the Old Street Road, must have appeared, to the least irrational new patient, like a chamber of horrors. What sane person indeed, seeing on his entrance into any place, gyves and manacles (however highly polished) yawning for his ankles and wrists; swings dangling in the air, to spin him round like an impaled cock-chafer; gags and strait-waistcoats ready at a moment's notice to muzzle and bind him; would be likely to retain the perfect command of his senses? Even now, an outside view of St. Luke's Hospital is gloomy enough; and, when on that cold, misty, cheerless afternoon which followed Christmas Day, I looked up at the high walls, and saw, grimly peering over them, its upper stories and dismal little iron-bound windows, I did not ring the porter's bell (albeit I was only a visitor, and free to go, if I would, without ringing it at all) in the most cheerful frame of mind.

"How came I, it may be asked, on the day after Christmas Day, of all days in the year, to be hovering outside Saint Luke's, after dark, when I might have betaken myself to that jocund world of Pantomime, where there is no affliction or calamity that leaves the least impression.

"Not long before the Christmas night in question, I had been told of a patient in St. Luke's, a woman of great strength and energy, who had been driven mad by an infuriated ox in the streets—an inconvenience not in itself worth mentioning, for which the inhabitants of London are frequently indebted to their inestimable Corporation. She seized the creature literally by the horns, and so, as long as limb and life were in peril, vigorously held him; but the danger over, she lost her senses, and became one of the most ungovernable of the inmates of the asylum. Why was I there to see this poor creature when I might have seen a Pantomimic woman gored to any extent by a Pantomimic ox, at any height of ferocity, and have gone home to bed with the comforting assurance, that she had rather enjoyed it than otherwise?

"The reason of my choice was this. I had received a notification that on that night there would be, in Saint Luke's 'A Christmas Tree for the Patients'. And further, that the 'usual fortnightly dancing' would take place before the distribution of the gifts upon the tree. So there I was, in the street, looking about for a knocker and finding none.

"Abandoning further search for the non-existent knocker, I discovered and rang the bell, and gained admission into Saint Luke's—through a stone courtyard and a hall, adorned with wreaths of holly and like seasonable garniture. I felt disposed to wonder how it looked to patients when they were first received, and whether they distorted it to their own wild fancies or left it a matter of fact. But, as there was time for a walk through the building before the festivities began, I discarded idle speculation, and followed my leader.

"Into a long, long gallery; on one side, a few windows; on the other a great many doors leading to sleeping cells. Dead silence—not utter solitude; for, outside the iron cage enclosing the fire-place between two of the windows, stood a motionless woman. The fire cast a red glare upon the walls, upon the ceiling, and upon the floor, polished by the daily friction of many feet. At the end of the gallery, the common sitting room. Seated on benches around another caged fire-place, several women; all silent except one. She, sewing a mad sort of seam, and scolding some imaginary person. (Taciturnity is a symptom of nearly every kind of mania unless under pressure of excitement, although the whole lives of some patients are passed together in the same apartment, they are passed in solitude; there is no solitude more complete.) Forms and tables, the only furniture. Nothing in the rooms to remind their inmates of the world outside. No domestic articles to occupy, to interest, or to entice the mind away from its malady. Utter vacuity. Except the scolding woman sewing a purposeless seam, every patient in the room either silently looking at the fire, or silently looking at the ground—or rather through the ground, and at Heaven knows what, beyond.

"It was a relief to come to a work-room; with coloured prints over the mantel-shelf, and china shepherdesses upon it; furnished also with tables, a carpet, stuffed chairs, and an open fire. I observed a great difference between the demeanour of the occupants of this apartment and that of the inmates of the other room. They were neither so listless nor so sad. Although they did not, while I was present, speak much, they worked with earnestness and diligence. A few noticed my going away, and returned my parting salutation. In a niche—not in a room—but at one end of a cheerless gallery—stood a pianoforte, with a few ragged music-leaves upon the desk. Of course the music was turned upside down.

"Several such galleries on the 'female side': all exactly alike. One set apart for 'boarders' who are incurable; and, towards whose maintenance their friends are required to pay a small weekly sum. The experience of this asylum did not differ, I found, from that of similar establishments, in proving that insanity is more prevalent among women than among men. Of the eighteen thousand seven hundred and fifty-nine inmates St. Luke's Hospital has received in the century of its existence, eleven thousand one hundred and sixty-two have been women, and seven thousand five hundred and eighty-seven, men. Female servants are, as is well known, more frequently afflicted with lunacy than any other class of persons. The table published in the Directors' Report of the condition in life of the one hundred and seven female inmates admitted in 1850, sets forth that while, under the vague description of 'wife of labourer' there were only nine admissions, and under the equally indefinite term 'housekeeper' no more than six; there were of women servants, twenty-four.

"I passed into one of the galleries on the male side. Three men, engaged at a game of bagatelle; another patient kneeling against the wall, apparently in deep prayer; two, walking rapidly up and down the long gallery arm-in-arm, but, as usual, without speaking together; a handsome young man deriving intense gratification from the motion of his fingers as he played with them in the air; two men standing like pillars before the fire-cage; one man, with a newspaper under his arm walking with great rapidity from one end of the corridor to the other, as if engaged in some important mission which admitted of not a moment's delay. The only furniture in the common sitting-room not peculiar to a prison or a lunatic asylum of the old school, was a news-paper, which was being read by a demented publican. The same oppressive silence—except when the publican complained, in tones of the bitterest satire, against one of the keepers, or (said the publican) 'attendant, as I suppose I must call him'. The same listless vacuity here as in the room occupied by the female patients. Despite the large amount of cures effected in the Hospital (upwards of sixty-nine per cent. during the past year), testifying to the general efficacy of the treatment pursued in it, I think that, if the system of finding the inmates employment, so successful in other hospitals, were introduced into Saint Luke's, the proportion of cures would be much greater. Appended to the latest report of the Charity is a table of the weights of the new-comers, compared with the weights of the same individuals when discharged. From this, it appears that their inactivity occasions a rapid accumulation of flesh. Of thirty patients, whose average residence in the Hospital extended over eleven weeks, twenty-nine had gained at the average rate of more than one pound per week, each. This can hardly be a gain of health.

"On the walls of some of the sleeping cells were the marks of what looked like small alcoves that had been removed. These indicated the places to which the chairs, which patients were made to sit in for indefinite periods, were, in the good old times, nailed. A couple of these chairs have been preserved in a lumber room, and are hideous curiosities indeed. As high as the seat, are boxes to enclose the legs, which used to be shut in with spring bolts. The thighs were locked down by a strong cross-board, which also served as a table. The backing of this cramping prison is so constructed that the victim could only use his arms and hands in a forward direction; not backward or sideways.

"Each sleeping cell has two articles of furniture—a bed and a stool; the latter serving instead of a wardrobe. Many of the patients sleep in single-bedded rooms; but the larger cells

63

are occupied by four inmates. The bedding is comfortable, and the clothing ample. On one bed-place the clothes were folded up, and the bedding had been removed. In its stead was a small bundle, made up of a pair of boots, a waistcoat and some stockings. '*That* poor fellow', said my conductor, 'died last night—in a fit.'

"As I was looking at the marks in the walls of the galleries, of the post to which the patients were formerly chained, sounds of music were heard from a distance. The Ball had begun, and we hurried off in the direction of the music.

"It was playing in another gallery—a brown, sombre place, now brilliantly illuminated by a light at either end, adorned with holly. The staircase by which this gallery was approached, was curtained off at the top, and near the curtain the musicians were cheerfully engaged in getting all the vivacity that could be got, out of their two instruments. At one end were a number of mad men, at the other a number of mad women, seated on forms. Two or three sets of quadrille dancers were arranged down the centre, and the ball was proceeding with great spirit, but with great decorum.

"There were the patients usually to be found in all such asylums, among the dancers. There was the brisk, vain, pippin-faced little old lady, in a fantastic cap—proud of her foot and ankle; there was the old-young woman, with the dishevelled long light hair, spare figure, and weird gentility; there was the vacantly-laughing girl, requiring now and then a warning finger to admonish her; there was the quiet young woman, almost well, and soon going out. For partners, there were the sturdy bull-necked thick-set little fellow who had tried to get away last week; the wry-faced tailor, formerly suicidal, but much improved; the suspicious patient with a countenance of gloom, wandering round and round strangers, furtively eyeing them behind from head to foot, and not indisposed to resent their intrusion. There was a man of happy silliness, pleased with everything. But the only chain that made any clatter was Ladies' Chain, and there was no straiter waistcoat in company than the polka garment of the old-young woman with the weird gentility, which was of a faded black satin, and languished through the dance with a lovelorn affability and condescension to the

force of circumstances, in itself a faint reflection of all
Bedlam.

"Among those seated on the forms, the usual loss of social
habits and the usual solitude in society, were again to be
observed. It was very remarkable to see how they huddled
together without communicating; how some watched the
dancing with lack-lustre eyes, scarcely seeming to know what
they watched; how others rested weary heads on hands, and
moped; how others had the air of eternally expecting some
miraculous visitor who never came, and looking out for
some deliverances that never happen. The last figure of the
set danced out, the woman-dancers instantly returned to their
station at one end of the gallery, the men-dancers repaired
to *their* station at the other; and all were shut up within
themselves in a moment.

"The dancers were not all patients. Among them, and
dancing with right good will, were attendants, male and
female—pleasant-looking men, not at all realising the
conventional idea of 'keepers'—and pretty women, gracefully
though not at all inappropriately dressed, and with looks
and smiles as sparkling as one might hope to see in any
dance in any place. Also there were sundry bright young
ladies who had helped to make the Christmas Tree; and a
few members of the resident officer's family; and shining
above them all, and shining everywhere, his wife; whose clear
head and strong heart Heaven inspired to have no Christmas
wish beyond this place, but to look upon it as her home, and
on its inmates as her afflicted children. And may I see
as seasonable a sight as that gentle Christian lady
every Christmas that I live, and leave its counterpart in as
fair a form in many a nook and corner of the world, to shine,
like a star in a dark spot, through all the Christmases to
come!

"The tree was in a bye room by itself, not lighted yet, but
presently to be displayed in all its glory. The porter of the
Institution, a brisk young fellow, with no end of dancing in
him, now proclaimed a song. The announcement being
received with loud applause, one of the dancing sisterhood
of attendants sang the song, which the musicians accompanied. It was very pretty, and we all applauded to the echo,
and seemed (the mad part of us I mean) to like our share in

the applause prodigiously, and to take it as a capital point that we were led by the popular porter. It was so great a success that we very soon called for another song, and then we danced a country dance (porter perpetually going down the middle and up again with weird-gentility) until the quaint pictures of the Founders hanging in the adjacent Committee-chamber, might have trembled in their frames.

"The moment the dance was over, away the porter ran, not in the least out of breath, to help light up the tree. Presently it stood in the centre of its room, growing out of the floor, a blaze of light and glitter; blossoming in that place (as the story goes of the American aloe) for the first time in a hundred years. O shades of Mad Doctors with laced ruffles and powdered wigs, O shades of patients who went mad in the only good old times to be mad or sane in, and who were therefore physicked, whirligigged, chained, handcuffed, beaten, cramped, and tortured, look from

'Wherever in your sightless substances
You wait—'

on this outlandish weed in the degenerate garden of Saint Luke's!

"To one coming freshly from outer life, unused to such scenes, it was a very sad and touching spectacle, when the patients were admitted in a line, to pass round the lighted tree, and admire. I could not but remember with what happy, hopefully-flushed faces, the brilliant toy was associated in my usual knowledge of it, and compare them with the worn cheek, the listless stare, the full eye raised for a moment and then confusedly dropped, the restless eagerness, the moody surprise, so different from the sweet expectancy and astonishment of children, that came in melancholy array before me. And when the sorrowful procession was closed by 'Tommy', the favourite of the house, the harmless old man with a giggle and a chuckle and a nod for everyone, I think I would have rather that Tommy had charged at the tree like a bull than that Tommy had been at once so childish and so dreadful unchildlike.

"We all went out into the gallery again after this survey, and the dazzling fruits of the tree were taken from their boughs and distributed. The porter, an undeveloped genius

66

in stage management and mastership of ceremonies, was very active in the distribution, blew all the whistles, played all the trumpets, and nursed all the dolls. That done, we had a wonderful concluding dance, compounded of a country dance and gallopade, during which all the popular couples were honoured with a general clapping of hands, as they galloped down the middle; and the porter in particular was overwhelmed with plaudits. Finally, we had 'God save the Queen', with the whole force of the Company; solo parts by the female attendant with the pretty voice who had sung before; chorus led, with loyal animation, by the porter. When I came away, the porter, surrounded by bearers of trays, and busy in the midst of the forms, was delivering out nuts and cake, like a banker dealing at a colossal round game. I daresay he was asleep before I got home; but I left him in that state of social briskness which is usually described among people who are at large, as 'beginning to spend the evening'.

"Now, there is doubtless a great deal that is mournfully affecting in such a sight. I close this little record of my visit with the statement that the fact is so, because I am not sure but that many people expect far too much. I have known some, after visiting the noblest of our Institutions for this terrible calamity, express their disappointment at the many deplorable cases they had observed with pain, and hint that, after all, the better system could do but little. Something of what it can do, and daily does, has been faintly shadowed forth, even in this paper. Wonderful things have been done for the Blind, and for the Deaf and Dumb; but the utmost is necessarily far inferior to the restoration of the senses of which they are deprived. To lighten the affliction of insanity by all human means is not to restore the greatest of the Divine gifts; and those who devote themselves to the task do not pretend that it is. They find their sustainment and reward in the substitution of humanity for brutality, kindness for mal-treatment, peace for raging fury; in the acquisition of love instead of hatred; and in the knowledge that from such treatment, improvement, and hope of final restoration will come, if such hope be possible. It may be little to have abolished from mad houses all that is abolished, and to have substituted all that is substituted.

Nevertheless, reader, if you can do a little in any good direction—do it. It will be much, some day."

Note by the Committee:

"CONTRAST BETWEEN 1852 and 1883"

"The preceding notice of St. Luke's Hospital, written by that keen observer the late Charles Dickens, appeared in *Household Words*, February, 1852.

"It contains an accurate and vivid description of St. Luke's at an eventful period of its history; it is now circulated in order to show the progress which the Hospital has made during the last Quarter of a Century, and to bring prominently before the public the contrast of its present improved condition.

"Mr. Dickens' graphic account of what St. Luke's was in 1852, shews the Executive of the Hospital cautiously entering on those reforms which had been previously established in other similar Institutions. He described the remains of the monastic treatment of the insane in the dismal iron-bound windows, the iron-caged fire-places, the scanty furniture, and the floor—only polished by the daily friction of many feet.

"The silence of the wards chills—the sadness and vacuity of the patients distress him. The only furniture in the common sitting-room, on the men's side, not peculiar to a prison of a Lunatic Asylum of the old school, is a solitary newspaper.

"Since Mr. Dickens' account appeared, much of this is changed; many of the defects have been supplied. The 'dismal', the 'vacant' and the 'sad', are no longer the characteristics of St. Luke's.

"1883 finds many of the cumbrous casements replaced by cheerful windows. Open fire-places have been substituted for the iron-caged grates, and handsome stuffed settees, covered with Utrecht velvet, for the rude benches of 1852. The tastefully-papered walls, everywhere hung with valuable engravings, the matted floor, and neat linoleum of the passages, give a very real air of home to the once naked galleries and day rooms.

" 'Happy families', well-managed Aquaria, Aviaries,

Books, the Daily Journals, the Weekly Illustrated Papers, and other serials, are everywhere at hand, and so far as such means can, relieve the monotony of durance.

"Of these sources of amusement the patients freely avail themselves; and their estimate of the confidence reposed in them, is shewn by the care bestowed on these perishable objects. The pleasant hum of many voices; the lively rattle of billiard and bagatelle balls; of dominoes and back-gammon, the notes of pianofortes, give a genuine and healthy gaiety to the scene. As a consequence of this cheerful domestic life, and of the air of home and comfort which pervades St. Luke's, the number of cures have steadily increased, more than *two-thirds* of the persons admitted being speedily restored to reason, and to the world.

"The Committee and their Officers are fully alive to the existing deficiences of the building and its fittings, but are unable, from the want of the necessary funds, to carry out their views of further improvement and reform. With sufficient aid, St. Luke's will become a model hospital for the cure of insanity. It is with the hope of obtaining these requisite means that this narrative is now circulated."

The Metropolitan Commissioners in Lunacy first visited St. Luke's in 1842, and five years later they summarised the results of their inspections. From the first they criticised both the site and design of the building. In view of the completely changed views and theories of the medical profession on the subject and the progress in the treatment of lunacy since the hospital was designed and built some 60 years previously, this was hardly surprising. Among other defects, the space available and interior arrangements made it impossible to classify the patients accurately, and the airing courts were both inadequate and ill-planned. The Commissioners regretted that large sums had been spent on improving a building in a situation "so objectionable", and they urged that it should be re-built in a more convenient and less depressing site. Their objections and criticisms reached a climax in March 1855 when the following report, signed by the Chairman, Lord Shaftesbury (formerly Lord Ashley), and two other Com-missioners after a special visit to the hospital was sent officially to the Committee. In this they wrote:

"On this, as on former occasions, we were struck with the cheerless and dreary aspect presented both within the building and in the airing courts.

"Few or no steps appear to have been taken to forward the recommendations made in previous reports as to out-door exercise, occupations and the purchase of land in the vicinity of London.

"Having regard to the irremediable defects in the present building and the many serious objections to the continued use of it for the reception of insane patients, we deem it our duty, instead of suggesting particular improvements, again to urge on all who are in any way responsible for the condition of this Charitable Institution to take into their consideration without loss of time the best means of obtaining suitable accommodation in a properly constructed building occupying an eligible situation.

"Whilst expressing our insuperable objections to the building itself, we think it right to state that, in consequence of the zeal and activity of the medical officers, as well as of other causes, the results as regards the number of patients discharged recovered are more satisfactory than might have been anticipated.[1] Nevertheless, we entertain a confident opinion that if the labours of the medical gentlemen were carried on under more favourable circumstances, their efforts would be more successful."

Here in fact was what amounted almost to an ultimatum which demanded—and received—a considered and decisive answer. In the following month the Committee sent their reply. Their opinion was that considering:

(1) the central position in London which would in any case require an Asylum if St. Luke's were moved elsewhere,

(2) the terms of the lease under which the site was held from St. Bartholomew's Hospital,

(3) the inadequacy of the funds available,

it would not conduce to the future prosperity of the Institution,

[1] The percentage of those discharged recovered was 71.15 in 1854 (Physicians' Report).

nor to the increasing number of patients, were the Committee to adopt the Commissioners' suggestions in regard to a building on which so vast a sum had been expended, and the proposed construction of a new asylum planned on the continually changing notions regarding design and on a supposedly more eligible site.

They pointed out that the internal arrangements and improvements of St. Luke's had for long occupied their attention. Its external appearance they agreed could be improved if only funds were available, but at present the income of the Charity was not enough even for actual maintenance of the Hospital.

They drew the attention of the Commissioners to the accessibility of St. Luke's for patients coming by rail, to the contentment of the inmates, to their good bodily health and to the large proportion of recoveries. Indeed, so suitable did they consider the hospital for curable cases that they might have to review the general question of receiving boarders, i.e., "incurable" cases as well.

Finally, they explained the terms of their lease, whereby, if the building now occupied by St. Luke's ceased to be a hospital, not only the land but the building and all fixtures would revert to St. Bartholomew's Hospital.

For these reasons the Committee respectfully declined to adopt the suggestions of the Commissioners, which they believed, if carried into effect, would close at once and forever an Institution which enjoyed the confidence of the Public and which had succeeded in restoring to mental health more than two-thirds of the patients who had been placed under its care.

Regret must be felt that apparently all this controversy was conducted on paper. There is little sign of any personal contact between the Commissioners and the Governors. Thus only could misunderstandings have been cleared away. Like some other social reformers the Commissioners showed either a magnificent disregard for finance or were completely ignorant of St. Luke's budget figures and annual accounts. If such disregard was the reason for their proposals it must have been a trial to the careful men who had nursed the hospital's funds for so many years, but if the Commissioners were ignorant of the state of St. Luke's financial position, the fault surely lay with the Governors for not making the position clear.

As regards the much abused site, the Committee had replied

with some effect. Could they have looked into the future and seen that the hospital would remain in Old Street and continue to do admirable work there for another sixty years, their answer might have been made even more conclusive. Whether it would have been possible in 1855 to have come to an arrangement mutually advantageous to both hospitals, such as was reached in 1916 after years of negotiation and very hard bargaining, and also to have found a purchaser for the site, it is impossible to say. Even could these results have been achieved in 1855, and could a new hospital have been built elsewhere, it is not certain whether it would have been better for the patients. Some authorities believed that they were unaffected by their surroundings. Many of them were Londoners and perhaps happier in and also overlooking the noise, bustle and even grime of the City than in what might have seemed to them a lonely and dreary countryside.

Despite the Committee's uncompromising reply, the Commissioners did not cease what may perhaps be justifiably described as their nagging objections to the site. But the Governors were on the whole supported by their physicians, who emphasised that St. Luke's was a hospital, and as such, questions concerning it affected all other metropolitan hospitals whose physicians and students could visit it. They admitted the difficulties and limitations of its position and plan which, to a certain extent, precluded moral and occupational treatment. Nevertheless, it seemed to them that since nearly three-quarters of the patients recovered, either the situation of an hospital for acute cases of insanity was not of such importance as some authorities supposed or that medical treatment, on which they largely depended, was generally underrated.

Although the site and design of the hospital were the main targets of the Commissioners' criticisms at this period, some of their other remarks on the shortcomings of St. Luke's deserved —and were given—consideration. The interior of the hospital was cold, cheerless and uncomfortable. Arrangements for the washing of patients were found to be defective, and the patients themselves were allowed to be slovenly and untidy in their dress. As had been proved elsewhere, this was harmful mentally. Neither their bedding nor their body linen was changed as often as it should be. The men were shaved only twice a week. Some patients still slept in wooden trough beds with only loose straw and blankets and the Commissioners strongly criticised the practice of throwing sheets over such beds in day-time and thus giving an entirely false air of comfort and cleanliness.

Gradually, however—and at considerable expense—improvements were carried out and even as early as 1852 the Commissioners admitted that there was much improvement throughout the hospital, although they regretted that so much had been spent on the building. They complained, and the complaint was frequently repeated, that there was not enough employment or amusement, particularly for the men. This was a matter in which no one seems to have shown much initiative or imagination, or to have realised that occupation was not merely desirable but an essential and vital part of the treatment in all mental cases. A few unsuccessful attempts were made to hire land on which the patients could have done some cultivation, but even if successful, it is questionable whether many of the men would have benefited by or appreciated manual labour. Today, everyone can and frequently does, use a spade. Judging by the lists of the occupations of male patients at that time it is doubtful if more than a small proportion of them had either worked in or owned a garden. Allotments for townsmen were then unknown. The Commissioners, however, seem to have been thoroughly rural-minded and firm believers in digging and in country surroundings for the patients. There is no evidence that they were groping towards some form of colony estate such as had been established in Belgium where patients were housed either in a number of small hostels or individually as lodgers with carefully selected cottagers. No such idea was, however, suggested to the Governors, and in any case, such a plan might not have been suitable for a hospital. In St. Luke's, some of the patients were tradesmen, and, despite the prejudices of those days, they and others might have been persuaded tactfully that a knowledge of a manual trade would not have been beneath their dignity. Other institutions had carpenters', tailors' and other shops and the physicians actually suggested that these might have been created in the basement, which, as the Commissioners frequently pointed out, were unfit for patients' accommodation. The Committee, however, were not at first favourable to this proposal and it took some years to persuade them to accept a trained carpenter and a plumber who was also a painter and glazier on the staff. These two were primarily for maintenance, and when practicable, they were allowed to employ patients to help them. This was at least a step towards occupation for the male patients, but it was a very short one, and very far from the creation of shops and any real form of occupational therapy. The patients themselves were reluctant and lethargic, and the physicians thought that any form of compulsion would be reminiscent of a prison régime. With the women, the Matron seems to have been far more successful, but they, of course, had many occupations which came naturally to them and which, incidentally, were useful to the Matron.

On the food the Commissioners always reported well. It was good and liberal, and in 1854 was further improved by giving cocoa and milk with bread and butter for breakfast instead of gruel, and tea with bread and butter for the women's supper. For dinner, meat was given on six days in the week, instead of three, meat soup being given on the seventh. Nearly all patients seem to have gained weight during their stay in hospital. In 1856 the Committee commented on the great increase in the amount of wine and spirits ordered by the medical officers. In their reply the physicians wrote:

"The experience of each succeeding year shows us that Insanity is in a great majority of cases an unerring symptom, often the earliest, of faulty nutrition, shewing itself generally before any organ of the body could be said, in ordinary pathological parlance, to be diseased. This defective nutrition may be the result of parental disease, excessive wear and tear, mental and bodily, deficiency of hygienic requisites, or vicious habits and practices. This is in all cases to be combated chiefly by means of a well assorted and liberal dietary, with such adjuncts as shall provoke an appetite, where perhaps for months none has been known. We trust that these stern requirements of exhausted nature will plead an excuse for the somewhat large consumption of wine, brandy, porter and cod liver oil."

The following report in October 1853 shows that the physicians as well as the Commissioners realised that there was room for improvement at St. Luke's. It followed a visit to

Bethlem with which there had always been some co-operation and friendly rivalry.

After thanking the Treasurer and other members of the Committee who had accompanied them to Bethlem, the physicians wrote:

"While we acknowledge the superiority of the arrangements at Bethlem in some respects, we cannot but think that a small expenditure of money would make St. Luke's equal if not superior to Bethlem. There does not appear that difference in the plan of the building and the arrangement of the galleries and sleeping rooms in the one which would render it impossible for great improvements of a like nature to be made in the other.

"We think that something might be done immediately, viz., furniture might be placed in the galleries of a description similar to that used at Bethlem, and a different classification might be made so as to separate the noisy patients more effectually from the more orderly ones.

"It does not appear advisable to place all the noisy patients in the same gallery, but means might be made to set apart the wings of each gallery for them. . . .

"The Basement story might immediately be converted into workshops; we might have a carpenter, plumber, tailor and shoemaker as paid servants of the hospital. . . .

". . . The number of attendants at Bethlem is as 1 to 9 and we should be glad of an increased staff, as our present one is not sufficient.

"If a night nurse were hired to undertake the night watch in each gallery as at Bethlem, we think this increase would be sufficient.

"The above improvements we think might be carried out at once without much expense . . . other matters require more deliberation, but we hope they will not be abandoned."

In 1854 the government and administration of the hospital were also severely criticised by Dr. J. C. Bucknill in an article in the *Journal of Mental Science* of which he was the Editor.

He wrote that there was far too much control by the Treasurer, that the medical staff had no opportunity of laying their difficulties before the general body of the Governors, for they conferred only with the House Committee, the members of which were appointed for five months and retired just when they began to realise the imperfection of the hospital.

He laid great stress on the fact that the Steward and not the Resident Medical Officer had the chief authority inside the hospital. It was recommended that there should be a "Resident Medical Superintendent" instead of an "Apothecary" or "Resident Medical Officer", and that paramount authority within the hospital should be his. It was implied that the position of Matron was unnecessary and that her duties should be placed "in commission" and divided between a head female attendant, a head cook and a laundress. The writer went on to make some superfluous and jocular remarks about matrons in general, suggesting among other things that they should be chosen by weight, the ideal being "A lady, fat, fair and forty, with a sweet voice and angelic temper." For these remarks the writer apologised subsequently and hastened to explain that they were not intended to be in any way personal.

The article concluded by agreeing that good work had been done, but that in every department except that of medical treatment St. Luke's was in the rear of English asylums and that what was needed there was "a Committee of earnest and intelligent men."

Dr. Bucknill admitted that his article was based largely on information supplied by Dr. Henry Stevens who had recently been appointed Apothecary and Resident Medical Officer. Apparently, however, Dr. Stevens had not quite grasped the system of administration, for the statement about the House Committee was, to put it bluntly, grossly inaccurate. This Committee was appointed annually for twelve months. They met once a week and were supposed to make a thorough inspection of the hospital at least once a month. Moreover, the membership of General and House Committees overlapped, and each body knew well what the other was doing. It was true that all the members did not attend every meeting, but a large committee does not necessarily conduce to efficient administration or to quick action. The Committee spent much, indeed most, of their time over the admission and discharge of patients and scrutiny of their papers, but they did not, as Dr. Bucknill implied, concern themselves with their maladies, save on the advice of their medical officers.

Curiously enough, the site of the hospital so frequently attacked by the Commissioners was defended, as Dr. Stevens asserted that its deficiencies were not felt by the patients, while its central locality was convenient, indeed essential, for both pupils and patients.

The result of this article was that a special meeting of the General Committee was called in January 1856 to consider a resolution of the House Committee respecting the conduct of Dr. Stevens who had "furnished reports and documents relating to the hospital to the editor of a public journal in which had appeared an article containing reflections upon the Governors and officers of the hospital", and further that the sentiments in this article agreed so remarkably with the opinions and criticisms frequently expressed by Dr. Stevens since his appointment, that it was thought that he was the author. This, however, he denied, although he produced the manuscript of an article about the hospital which he had written but which had been refused by the Editor of the *Journal of Mental Science*.

The General Committee, having considered the matter, expressed its displeasure at an officer of the hospital having sent, without permission, documents of a private nature to a public journal, and cautioned their Apothecary to act with greater circumspection in future. It will probably be agreed that Dr. Stevens got off lightly.

Whether the Commissioners had studied Dr. Bucknill's article is not known, but it is a fact that subsequently they pressed strongly for the appointment of a Resident Medical Superintendent, with paramount authority within the hospital, a suggestion which the Governors only partially accepted in 1856.

Presumably Dr. Stevens' energy and skill outweighed his indiscretion and criticisms of the hospital, as he was appointed Medical Superintendent and earned high praise from the Commissioners for his work at St. Luke's when he retired in 1860.

The Commissioners also suggested that it should be a rule that the Treasurer should have no control over the Medical Superintendent but the Committee resisted this proposal, pointing out that in the intervals between Committee Meetings there must be someone to whom the Superintendent, the Steward, or the Matron could refer in case of need.

In short, according to both the Commissioners and Dr. Bucknill, what was good was due to the doctors and what was bad was the fault of the Governors. The truth probably was that in some respects the administration of St. Luke's was conservative. This may have been due in some measure to the great length of time during which the government and interior administration of the hospital were in the same hands. David and John Clark Powell held the Treasurership between them for 49 years. Mr. Dunston was Master and Superintendent for 49 years and Mr. Stinton for 26 years, while three generations of Websters were Secretaries for 99 years.

Reforms were not always carried out as quickly as young, ardent, and occasionally intolerant medical officers like Dr. Stevens may have wished. Nevertheless many of them were carried out as Dr. Bucknill admitted in a subsequent article.

On the whole there is no doubt that the inspections by the Commissioners were of great value to St. Luke's. Their criticisms were sometimes meticulous and their suggestions impracticable, but their visits prevented the Committee from growing over-complacent on the strength of 100 years' existence and a deservedly high reputation.

During the period 1850-1860, constant anxiety was felt concerning finance. In their Report for 1858 the Committee told the Governors that they had been compelled to sell over £17,000 of Stock since the centenary year and that quite apart from structural and other improvements, the annual cost of maintaining the hospital now exceeded the income of the Charity by over £1,000. A special Committee on Finance was appointed and in April 1858 issued a report to the following effect.

That during the past seven years, receipts from all sources had been gradually diminishing, while expenditure under every head had increased. The reduced income resulted from the smaller number of "Boarders", the non-admission of pauper patients, both of whom contributed something towards their cost, and to the decrease in dividends caused by the sales of the funded capital in order to pay for structural improvements, and to meet current expenditure.

The average annual expenditure under the heading House Expenses, which did not include Wages and Salaries, in the years 1848-1850 was £3,819, while the average for 1855-1857 was £6,019.

The causes of such increases were:

  (i) The adoption in 1854 of a more generous and expensive diet.

 (ii) The increased cost of provisions.

(iii) Extra expenditure on comforts, such as furniture and decorations, improved bedding and a better warming and ventilating system.

(iv) Increased expenditure on "sick and extra diet" for patients admitted in a debilitated condition.

For instance, the average annual expenditure on wine, brandy, etc., from 1844 to 1849 was about £24; from 1849 to 1853 it was about £65, while the average annual cost of these stimulants during the four years previous to 1858 had been about £268. The consumption of beef tea and similar extras was also very much greater than formerly. These extras were due to the increased number of sick and weak patients who had been admitted during recent years.

No change in the general diet was recommended and it was hoped that the gradual fall in the price of provisions observable since 1851 would continue. It was considered that further heavy expenditure on structural improvements and additional furniture would no longer be necessary.

The Committee felt that in the matter of "sick and extra diet" they could not make suggestions as this was a matter for the medical officers.

In conclusion they regretted that they could not give a more favourable report on the position. They were of opinion that they could not count on additional support from the public and that the only way in which income could be increased would be to admit private patients whose friends could pay something towards their cost. The drain on the funded property must cease, and expenditure must no longer exceed income. They therefore recommended that the number of patients should be reduced and that the rule whereby in-curable cases were admitted as "boarders" at fees below the cost of supporting them be suspended.

On this report it was decided to admit patients whose friends could pay 21s. a week towards their cost, and also to arrange for removal of hopeless and incurable cases who could derive no possible benefit by remaining at St. Luke's to some country asylum where fresh and bracing air and more extended and varied exercise might possibly do them good.

Such a case was a man who had been 12 years in the hospital. He was very dirty in his habits and tended to annoy and disgust all the more treatable patients. Moreover, he could only speak Welsh and barely understood English. (Medical treatment must, therefore, have been difficult and moral treatment impossible, in this particular case.)

Other pathetic cases were those of the hopelessly insane who had outlived all their relations. These also were, in the opinion of the medical officers, better out of St. Luke's.

The results of this report with its impeccable financial recommendations, were economies in house expenses, increases in charges and more and larger donations. In 1860 not only did income exceed expenditure, but a loan of £1,000 was repaid.

While the Governors thus struggled successfully to put their financial house in order, the Commissioners in 1858, while reporting favourably on the improvements throughout the hospital, concluded with these words:

> "Considering the large amount of funded property, (upwards of £150,000), belonging to the institution, we think that the Committee might venture to establish a branch of the Hospital in the neighbourhood of London."

One can only suppose that the Commissioners had studied the Balance Sheet, but not the income and expenditure account.

By 1860 St. Luke's was a much improved institution. The long gloomy galleries had been divided into wards, and there were open and well-lighted recesses where the patients assembled for recreation. A Chapel, an amusement hall, and work-rooms had been provided; laundries and lavatories had been improved; steam boilers conveyed steam and hot water to all parts of the building. The hospital was now heated throughout by large open stoves and the wards had been reasonably furnished and decorated; the patients were given books, periodicals and games and their diet, already good and liberal, had been improved. Some of the airing courts had been enlarged, and the basement cells were no longer inhabited by "the more afflicted patients", but had been converted into workshops, coal cellars and foul-laundry rooms.

It is possible that in the past the Governors had never settled clearly in their minds whether St. Luke's was to be a hospital or an asylum. Once they admitted incurable cases (who incidentally paid a considerable proportion of their cost), they changed the whole character of the Institution. It had been started as "a Hospital for Lunatics", and a lunatic was, in the simple language then used by members of the medical profession who specialised in this disease, a person who was curable. More than once the hospital physicians emphasised that St. Luke's was a hospital, and there seems no doubt that that was what they wished it to be. They did not want these hopeless long-term cases and were quite clearly of the opinion that they might do better in country surroundings.

As a rule the Governors followed the advice and rarely disagreed with the treatment of their medical officers. One such disagreement was over the desirability or otherwise of the cold plunge bath treatment. In 1856 the physicians made a report in which they wrote that they did not think it advisable entirely to do away with them as they were "generally acknowledged to be an important means of treatment in some forms of insanity". They advised, however, that the existing bath should be improved and that the corners and edges should be covered with some soft material so that the patient should not hurt themselves and that patients before being "thrown into the water" should be as nearly as possible on a level with it. That no bath should be given without a written order from one of the medical staff and that the medical superintendent, the steward or the matron (if on the female side) should be present.

Despite this report, the Committee ordered the use of the cold plunge bath to be suspended until they had made enquiries about the practice in other establishments. These enquiries showed that it was not used as part of the treatment at either Bethlem or Colney Hatch as it excited terror and was considered as a punishment. It was believed that St. Luke's was the only place where it was still used. And so this treatment came to an end.

It would be interesting to discover whether this decision was based on the prevailing idea of more humane treatment of lunatics and whether in fact the physicians at St. Luke's were not right in believing that it did good in some cases.

VI

THE HOSPITAL'S CRITICS. FINANCIAL PROBLEMS AND REFORMS

IN 1860 Dr. A. J. Sutherland, the senior physician, resigned owing to ill health, after 19 years service. He was succeeded by Dr. Henry Monro, who had been at St. Luke's since 1851, and Doctor William Wood was elected second physician. Dr. Stevens (who had always criticised the administration and management of the hospital and been a thorn in the side of the Committee but a favourite of the Commissioners) also retired this year and was succeeded as Resident Medical Superintendent by Dr. Ebenezer Toller.

Although the attendants were always praised by the medical officers, it was implied that their standard was not as high as was desirable. They ought to have more definite qualifications than, in some cases, a little experience and an aptitude for dealing with the insane. This lack of such qualifications had been deplored, and the question of special training for mental attendants and nurses had been raised in Parliament by Lord Shaftesbury. The Commissioners also criticised the attendants, particularly the men. They said that they were changed so often that there was no time to train them. Both the medical officers and the Commissioners agreed that higher wages were not enough to secure and retain efficient persons. Moreover, at St. Luke's some of the attendants were overworked owing to the practice of doubling day and night duty. By this arrangement a man or a woman might be on duty occasionally from 6 a.m. on one day until 8 p.m. the next, i.e., for 38 hours with only 4 hours rest. The women nurses were better than the men. This was probably due to the then Matron, Mrs. Walker, who was able to give more time to the patients than did the Steward who was "cumbered about with much serving".

The staff of the hospital in 1868 consisted of the following:
Officers: 2 Physicians, 1 Surgeon, the Chaplain and the Secretary. The Resident Medical Superintendent, the Steward, Matron and Dispenser.

Attendants: Male—7 and 1 Night Attendant.

Female—12 and 1 Night Attendant.

Servants: Male—Gate Porter and two Assistants, 1 Cutter of Provisions, 1 Carpenter, 1 Engineer, 1 Painter (who was also Plumber and Glazier).

Female—1 Needlewoman, 3 Housemaids, 1 Head Laundress and 5 Laundry Maids, 1 Cook and 1 Kitchen Maid.

The scale of Pay for the Attendants varied according to length of service and was:

Male: 3 at £32 10s. 0d. per annum

1 „ £28 10s. 0d. „   „

3 „ £27 10s. 0d. „   „

1 Night Attendant at £32 10s. 0d. per annum

Female: 1 at £24 0s. 0d. per annum

1 „ £21 0s. 0d. „   „

7 „ £20 0s. 0d. „   „

3 „ £18 0s. 0d. „   „

1 Night Attendant at £28 0s. 0d. per annum

At this time, however, the main preoccupation of the Committee was finance. Despite the rise in fees expenditure still exceeded income. Sometimes this gnawing anxiety about money caused an appearance of hardness and rigidity as when they refused any relaxation in the case of a patient, whose sisters wrote as follows:

"Gentlemen, . . . We desire to address you on behalf of our poor sister, who, for the last 10 years has been an inmate of your asylum and, during the whole of that period the sum of one guinea weekly has been paid by our dear Father, amounting (in all) to £532 7s. 0d., but, from his advanced age (79 years) and declining health, we feel that the pressure of this, added to other afflictions, is too much for him and that he is giving way under it. We, therefore, humbly pray your honourable Board to examine the case and kindly offer such relief as you may think proper to grant."

On the other hand there were cases where the relations were distinctly mean, as was the son of an elderly female patient on the 7s. scale. He was discovered to be the owner of a considerable outfitting shop and also some house property. This man not only said that he could not afford more than 7s. a week but sent his mother to the hospital without decent or suitable clothing. The Committee rightly demanded—and were paid—14s. a week in future.

The Commissioners, while giving the Committee credit for improvements inside the hospital, remained critical. They said that the patients should have more and better furniture and that the galleries were still very gloomy, but structural alterations in this old and out-of-date building were, they considered, a waste of money. They noted that there were fewer patients, "due probably to the objectionable locality". They discovered in 1861 that two patients were allowed to have a hot bath simultaneously, but this undesirable practice, due to a lack of hot water and to unnecessarily large baths, was stopped at once. A few years later smaller baths and two new "Cornish" boilers to a great extent overcame the hot water difficulty.

The Commissioners, year in, year out, pressed for more occupation and amusement for the male patients. The desirability of finding ways that would relieve the monotony of their lives was strongly urged. They asserted (wrongly, as a matter of fact) that only once a year was there a general meeting of both sexes for recreation. (There were fortnightly dances certainly from 1850 onwards.) The sexes, they complained, never met at meals. The billiard table and bowling green were rarely used; indeed the former was in such a state of disrepair that it would have given no amusement to have attempted to play on it.

The Governors had tried to improve matters in these respects. They had given grants and had provided pianos, bagatelle tables, and so forth, while individual Governors had presented pictures, books and birds in cages.

But about this time there are indications of a loss of interest in the hospital among the Governors generally. The Treasurer and a few Governors were assiduous in their attendance at Committee meetings, but there were many occasions on which there was no quorum.

The Governors were supposed to visit and inspect the hospital periodically. But in the Commissioners' Report of 1869 it was stated:

'As regards visitation and management . . . the House Committee meet at the Hospital every Friday to receive applications for the admission of patients, and at least once a month they are required to inspect every part of the Hospital and record in a book kept for that purpose the condition in which they find the establishment, together with suggestions for improvement, such as may have occurred to them during inspection. And a like inspection is to be made at some uncertain time at least once in three months by one or more members of the (General) Committee. How far these important duties are performed we had no means of ascertaining with accuracy, but the last three records of inspection are dated the 7th of August, the 23rd of October, and the 24th of December in the past year, and these entries contain no suggestions for improvements."

To this report there was no recorded reply beyond a minute to the effect that the Committee approved an answer drafted by the Medical Officers.

As regards occupation and amusement, the Governors did what they could. But they were hampered at this time by their financial difficulties, and always by lack of co-operation on the part of the patients and by a lack of imagination generally on the subject. Caged birds and pictures may give amusement to some persons for a limited period, but for the patients at St. Luke's it was necessary that occupation and amusement should be regularly organised. Many patients were listless and hard to lead, and the medical officers thought it would be better not to drive them, as that would savour of a prison régime. Why the Governors did not, or would not, accept the suggestion of the medical officers, after their visit to Bethlem in 1853, to have workshops in the basement is nowhere explained.

Never was the need for an Occupational Therapist (whatever he or she might have been called) more necessary. But such an appointment would have been ahead of the times. Meanwhile what was everyone's business was left undone. Today most people realise that any man or woman without some hobby or handicraft outside their daily work is as a rule seriously handicapped for the enjoyment of life. This does not seem to have been the case among the serious-minded and earnest Victorians. Anyone who practised carpentry in his spare time would probably have been considered eccentric, while a man who did needlework would have been thought either effeminate or suitable for an asylum.

At this period the Resident Medical Superintendent, with an average of 140 patients to look after, the Chaplain, who was also the Secretary, and the Steward, were all too busy to devote much time to finding work or play for the men. For the women the Matron managed to do a great deal; she was better supported by the nurses and the women were obviously easier to manage. On the male side there does not seem to have been anyone, apart of course from the Medical Superintendent, other than the Steward to oversee and inspire the male attendants, for a head male attendant was not appointed until 1882.

In any case there was still divided authority within the hospital. The revised regulations of 1856 had laid down that the Resident Medical Superintendent should, subject to the General and House Committees, have paramount authority over every officer resident in the hospital in respect of the medical and moral treatment of the patients, and should be responsible for the general condition of the hospital. But there were other rules and customs which modified and divided his authority. The then Resident Medical Superintendent had raised this question with the Committee and a special Sub-Committee was appointed to consider the respective responsibilities of the chief officers. They eventually presented a most elaborate and detailed report in which they concluded that the existing rules laid down very clearly the distinct spheres of duty of the chief resident officers "who were not responsible to each other", but each was under the control of the General and House Committee. They saw no reason why the Resident Medical Superintendent "should be put in command of the whole establishment. There was", they said, "plenty of scope of action for each of the four chief officers . . . and neither of them need come in conflict with the other if each bore in mind the limit of their duty . . . and exercised a little kindness and forebearance towards each other." In their opinion the duties of the several officers were as clearly defined as was possible where all were members of one establishment, and they advised them to adopt a "conciliatory line of conduct for the advantage of the institution and their own comfort". These were admirable sentiments which might also have been borne in mind by the

Committee and the Commissioners. From an administrative point, however, the greater the number of heads of departments who have thus to combine for the common good, the greater becomes the difficulty of smooth and united action, and the more essential does it become to have a controlling and co-ordinating authority. The Commissioners flatly disagreed with the conclusions of the Sub-Committee. They wrote that the Board had been led to expect that their views, and those of the Governors, were already in agreement about the re-organisation of the Staff and the increased powers of the Medical Superintendent. They were surprised that little or no change in these respects had been made or contemplated since 1856. They found it was unnecessary to repeat the arguments so often expressed in favour of giving in all asylums the sole and paramount authority and responsibility to the Resident Medical Officer. St. Luke's was the only hospital where this had not been done. The Commissioners concluded by asserting that the very unsatisfactory condition of the hospital which they found both on the latest visit and on many previous occasions was proof that their view was correct. On the other hand, the Committee probably could not forget the days when the Medical Superintendent was merely the Apothecary, and as such, low in the hospital hierarchy. They probably still con-sidered that the Treasurer should act as referee between the heads of departments. This would have been as impossible as it was undesirable and had already been firmly rejected by the Commissioners. They were fighting for a system which obtains to this day and has stood the test of time in mental hospitals, namely that everything which affects the patients directly or indirectly is the concern of the Medical Super-intendent. Needless to say this throws a heavy burden on this officer who requires to be both an efficient administrator and the leader of a team, as well as a specialist in this branch of medicine. And whatever he is, his institution will reflect him.

The Report of 1869 spoke well of the food, but pointed out that twice in the week meat soup was the only meat course at dinner, and that such a mid-day meal was not such as patients paying a guinea a week might expect. Potatoes were given all the year round, other vegetables being served very rarely.

The patients' diet had been revised in 1868 and was as under:

BREAKFAST

Every day: Males—Cocoa, 8 oz. Bread with Butter.
Females—Cocoa, 6 oz. Bread with Butter.

DINNER

Sunday: Males—8 oz. Cooked Meat with bone, 6 oz. Bread, 1 lb. Vegetables, 1 pt. Beer.
Females—6 oz. Cooked Meat with bone, 6 oz. Bread, $\frac{1}{2}$ lb. Vegetables, $\frac{1}{2}$ pt. Beer.
Monday: As on Sunday.
Tuesday: 1 pt. Meat Soup, 6 oz. Bread, 1 pt. Beer.
Wednesday: Males—8 oz. Cooked Meat, Rice, 1 pt. Beer.
Females—6 oz. Cooked Meat, Rice, $\frac{3}{4}$ pt. Beer.
Thursday: As on Sunday.
Friday: Males—Meat Pudding or Stew, 6 oz. Bread, 1 pt. Beer.
Females—Meat Pudding or Stew, 6 oz. Bread, $\frac{3}{4}$ pt. Beer.
Saturday: As on Sunday.

SUPPER

Every day: Males—8 oz. Bread, 2 oz. Cheese, $\frac{3}{4}$ pt. Beer.
Females—8 oz. Bread, Butter and Tea.

On these quantities it is not surprising that most of the patients gained in weight during their stay at St. Luke's, but the meals certainly did not do much to relieve the monotony of their lives, quite apart from the fact that the food lacked the vitamins considered essential according to modern ideas. The Commissioners recommended occasional puddings and fish and more frequently green vegetables as well as potatoes.

Later in 1869 in a letter to the Committee, the Commissioners expressed their satisfaction with the promises of improvement held forth by the Committee, and trusted that they will "with the least possible delay deal with the difficulties of their position." What exactly was meant by this somewhat ambiguous phrase it is impossible to tell, for the whole correspondence unfortunately was not recorded.

In the Commissioners' Report of the following year the conditions and appearance of the patients were found to have improved considerably, but means of occupation and amusement were still lacking. The diet had been altered, solid meat dinners being given instead of the soup formerly criticised, and green vegetables were to be allowed three times a week.

A new Medical Superintendent, Dr. Eager, had been appointed, but no alteration had been made in rules defining his duties as promised by the Committee.

The Commisioners were not the only critics of the hospital. In 1869 and 1870 severe attacks were made by *The Times* on the management of St. Luke's. They began with a letter signed by "A Well-wisher of St. Luke's" in December 1868. In this some of the criticisms of the Commissioners about the lack of entertainments, the disadvantages of the site and building and the inadequacy of the nursing service at night were repeated. It was stated that these were wholly disregarded. It asserted that the Treasurer, who considered himself fully competent to administer the Charity in all its details, had, in the past two years, presided at less than 50 per cent. of the weekly Committee Meetings.

This was quite true. The Treasurer was automatically a member of the House Committee; but there were other members who attended by rota. In 1869, after this letter, the Treasurer attended 41 meetings out of a possible 52.

Another anonymous communication followed in February 1869. This attacked the administration and the Committee, who, by "strenuous mismanagement", had not only reduced donations but had in 18 years sold out £23,000 of their funded property to meet current expenses. As for the Treasurer, "the virtual ruler of the hospital", he was determined to be guided only by the light of his own unaided judgment and had ignored both the recommendations of the Commissioners and the medical knowledge at his own disposal.

In April of that year these communications were followed by a special article in which the state and management of St. Luke's were condemned. Sir George Hodgkinson (a member of the Committee) had written to *The Times* saying that he could corroborate a great deal of the original letter. It was also asserted they had dismissed their Medical Superintendent on the plea that he had attended a private patient, but really because they wanted to get rid of his reforming zeal.

The actual government of St. Luke's, it stated, was anomalous, if not illegal. It ought to be under the control of the Resident Medical Superintendent, whereas the Steward and

D 89

Matron, if not actually emancipated from his direction, were in fact his rivals in authority and were always supported by the Committee, while the Visiting Physicians and Surgeon, "who could have no proper status" were treated as his superiors. The article concluded by asserting that St. Luke's was dirty and gloomy, that "the old wooden trough beds were still in use, and that there was no colour, no pictures, and no ornament in the hospital", and that the Committee had taken away from the paying boarders certain little matters of wine and extra diet to which they were accustomed.

All this was repeated in a leading article in February 1870. According to this, the hospital was in a worse financial position than ever. There was no evidence of vigour in the management. More of the invested funds had been sold, and ever since 1848 the Commissioners had made the same complaints about gloom, dirt, trough beds, lack of furniture and deficiency of hot water.

The Committee wrote to the Editor protesting against the "unfair and garbled statements" in the paper, and they also appealed to the Lord Chancellor asking him to have an independent enquiry made regarding the state of the hospital. But nothing came of this. The Lord Chancellor refused, because the matter might come before him judicially, and, when assured by the Committee that there was no likelihood of this, he still refused on the ground that he was not the Visitor to the hospital.

It is clear that the Committee, and particularly the Treasurer, had at least three critics with inside information, namely two ex-Superintendents and a member of the Committee, and it is probable that they stimulated the attack of *The Times* and supplied the ammunition rather as John Bold stimulated *The Jupiter* in the case of Hiram's Hospital.

The Governors had brought some of this trouble on their own heads. Year after year the Commissioners' complaints and recommendations were repeated and, if not ignored, were only partially and slowly remedied, and there are no recorded reasons given to the Commissioners or set forth in the minutes for this dilatory action, except for complaints of lack of funds. As regards the status of the Resident Medical Superintendent, they seem to have been both ill-advised and obstinate, and it is to be wondered that the Commissioners did not take the same high-handed action that they did 36 years later and warn the Governors that their regulations would not be approved by the Secretary of State until they had complied with the request of the Commissioners. The Governors would, of course, have been wise to have appointed a first-class physician to the position, and then supported him instead of clinging to their original system.

Many of the complaints and statements in *The Times* were overstated, but that is only to be expected if they depended on the statements of the reformers, who are apt to exaggerate the evils they wish to abolish.

When the Lord Chancellor refused to hold an enquiry it might have been supposed that the Board of the Commissioners in Lunacy was the proper and obvious body to which the Governors would have appealed for protection, for though critical, they were always just. But presumably the unhappy relations which the Committee had allowed to develop with them precluded an appeal to that quarter, and no enquiry was held and the matter dropped.

The whole story of this dual control by the Commissioners and the Governors is rather lamentable. The intentions and aims of both bodies were identical and had they been able to co-operate, both the patients and the hospital would have been the gainers. It is evident that mistakes were made by both parties. The Governors were conservative and suspicious, the Commissioners disregarded the limitations of finance in their desire to achieve quickly what they regarded as perfection. But above all, what was needed was the establishment of friendly personal relations. A full and frank discussion of aims and difficulties would have swept away more trouble than 10 years of reports and letters such as are recorded in the archives of the hospital.

It must not be thought, however, that because during the years after 1865 some of the Governors had been lax in their attendance at Committee Meetings, and the Commissioners had been critical about some aspects of the administration, no advance was made. Indeed, if the physicians' reports were the only ones on record, the period was one of progress and success. Of the curable patients admitted, the percentage of those discharged cured was 64. All patients increased in weight and the general health was good. One or two cases are worth recording. One female boarder died of cancer having spent 36 years of her life in St. Luke's. Two other cases are specially mentioned in these words:

"A clerk was brought to the Hospital on the recommendation of the Commissioners in Lunacy, he having been under treatment for a long period without benefit; the form of disease under which he laboured was melancholia; his anguish of mind was at times very painful to witness, he refused food and was in a deplorable condition; after five months residence, a marked improvement in his state became observable, and in seven months from the date of his admission he was dismissed on trial for a month with his friends, at the expiration of which period he was finally discharged cured.

"The other case was also that of another clerk; he was placed by his friends as a Boarder in this Institution in May last, being deemed hopelessly insane, his illness having extended over two years and a half; the form of insanity in this case also was melancholia; in a short time he was much improved, his depression vanished, he became cheerful, entered with zest into the amusements provided, and within a few months of his admission accompanied the other patients in their walks . . . he suffered no relapse, and in November was deemed sufficiently well to go out on trial; he left for a month and returned benefitted by the change, and was then discharged cured; a recovery so unexpected was welcomed with gratitude by his friends, who addressed a letter of heartfelt thanks to the Committee."

It is evident, therefore, that though there may have been some shortcomings in the administration, the Medical Officers, whose relations with the Governors were always excellent and co-operative, were able to effect a high proportion of cures, some of which were remarkable. In the circumstances it is not surprising that in 1866 the Senate of the University of London decided that they were willing to receive the certificates granted by the physicians for attendance on the medical practice of St. Luke's, for the purposes of graduation in medicine in the University.

After long negotiations the Committee were able to report

in 1868 that the Diocesan Registrar had given his sanction to the use of the Old Burial Ground as an addition to the airing ground and that they had rented it from the parish of St. Luke's for £30 a year. This area had for long been both a cause of offence, as the physicians considered that the sight of funerals was depressing for the patients, and a Naboth's Vineyard, as the Committee coveted the ground for open air exercise and recreation. Some years previously the Bishop of London had been persuaded to forbid any more burials there and now at last the area was added to St. Luke's. Apparently there were no gravestones or other memorials, but it cost £1,500 to combine this area with the existing airing ground.

A curious legal question arose in 1866. Lord Henry Seymour had left a considerable sum of money to be divided between hospitals in London and Paris, subject to certain life interests. Among the London hospitals were included the "Hospices des Lunatics de Londres", for the will was apparently drawn up in French. The matter had come before the Master of the Rolls, who had excluded St. Luke's from all benefits under the will because his opinion was that no charity was entitled to participate in the bequest unless every patient within its walls is received and maintained gratuitously, and he took a further ground against St. Luke's because the patients were not dealt with for the purposes of permanent occupation. On this interpretation of the word "Hospice" several other hospitals were also affected. Moreover, on a special legacy in this same will the Master of the Rolls decided in favour of Bethlem, to the exclusion of St. Luke's, not only on the ground of his interpretation of "Hospice", but also "because Bethlem was the older hospital of the two". This latter reason, argued Mr. Few, the hospital's solicitor, and also a Governor, could not be supported on any sound principle.

It was decided, therefore, to appeal with the other hospitals concerned. The ruling and interpretation was upset, and eventually St. Luke's benefited by a very considerable sum.

In 1869 the Rev. T. H. Cole was appointed Chaplain and Secretary. He seems to have realised at once that something drastic had to be done to increase the income of the hospital, and by the end of the year had devised the following scheme which was accepted by the Committee:

93

(1) That curable cases, not admissible as free patients, be admitted at 14s., 21s. and 30s. per week, respectively.
(2) That chronic cases be admitted at 21s. and 30s. per week.
(3) That incurables, viz., those who have been one year in the hospital be transferred either to the 14s., 21s. or 30s. list according to the circumstances.

It was agreed at the same time that curable patients might not reside in the hospital for longer than eighteen months.

This scheme of higher fees on a sliding scale proved successful and enabled the Committee to put an end to the depletion of the General Fund and brought to an end the difficult and harassing decade, 1860-1869.

VII

SUGGESTIONS FOR A MOVE OUT OF THE CITY.
SOME ADMINISTRATIVE PROBLEMS

AFTER 1870 times were more tranquil than during the
somewhat difficult period immediately preceding that
year. While full of interest, the undercurrent of irritation, due partly to the occasionally hypercritical attitude of
the Commissioners, though mainly to the gnawing anxiety felt
by the Committee about the financial position of St. Luke's,
is no longer discernible in the records.

The revised system of fees adjusted on a sliding scale and
devised by the Secretary-Chaplain, the Rev. T. H. Cole, proved
a success. In the five years before 1870 the average amount
received annually from patients was £3,228, in the five years
after that date the average rose to over £6,000. A number of
patients were admitted free by the House Committee which
acted collectively as almoners, and the Commissioners were at
pains to point out more than once that St. Luke's was, therefore,
fully entitled to be considered a charity.

Moreover, this sliding scale of fees actually proved to be a
stimulus to applications for admission.

The hospital was so full in 1874 and 1875 that extra accommodation was necessary, and the Committee, with whom the
Commissioners were in full agreement, decided to appoint
two resident Clinical Assistants. It was recognised that the
duties of the Resident Medical Superintendent were becoming
so heavy and exacting that, even with the assistance of the
visiting medical staff, he could no longer cope with them single-
handed.

Despite the increase in patients, house expenses were kept
down. The Treasurer reported in 1872 that the rise in expenditure during the previous six years had been due in large
measure to extras for patients who were sick and had been
admitted in a weak and debilitated condition. The Medical
Staff were asked to suggest economies in this direction. They
reported that there had been a certain amount of waste, and

suggested, somewhat pointedly, that the ward diet sheets should be seen every month by the Committee. They also recommended a few changes, including the use of Liebig's Ramornie Extract of Beef, which had recently been put on the market and was said to have nutritive and restorative properties and to be easily and quickly made. When farinaceous puddings were given, usually once a week, they thought that the meat on that day might be reduced to six ounces for men and four for women.

The Commissioners continued to criticise whenever and wherever they found cause. Rightly they would not be satisfied with anything less than the best, but there was no longer the note of exasperation in their reports at St. Luke's being out-of-date in its construction and ill-placed in its situation. Indeed, generally speaking they admitted steady improvement in every direction. In 1871, much to their satisfaction, patients were given green vegetables three times a week and for the first time were allowed mustard and vinegar.

They reported that both the wings and the wards were lighter and more cheerful, though the former, on the men's side, still lacked some amenities. "As long as barred windows exist in the Hospital", they wrote, "these must be a constant reminder of imprisonment, but at least they should be kept clean." A few years later 50 windows were enlarged and the bars presumably abolished.

As a rule the Commissioners found that complaints of ill-treatment by the attendants were without any foundation. In one case a man who complained was himself the assailant, and the attendant, whom he accused, was at the time of the complaint a patient in St. Bartholomew's, very seriously ill from a kick by this man.

A later report made by other Commissioners stated that there had been some complaints, but they had not been able to find what was the truth. They added, however, that when such complaints were made by patients in different wards, who could have had no communication with each other, there was an uncomfortable impression that the charges might not be absolutely unfounded.

These were not of course the only instances where the reports varied both in emphasis and in the points raised. This was inevitable when visitations were made by different persons

DR. THOMAS CROWE, M.D.

PRINCIPAL FOUNDER AND FIRST VICE-PRESIDENT

PLATE II

Dr. William Battie, M.D.
VISITING PHYSICIAN, 1750-1764.

PLATE III

DR. SAMUEL FOART SIMMONS, F.R.S., M.D.
VISITING PHYSICIAN, 1781-1811.

PLATE IV

DR. ALEXANDER ROBERT SUTHERLAND, M.D.
VISITING PHYSICIAN, 1811-1841.

PLATE V

THE RT. HON. THE DUKE OF MONTAGU, K.G., F.R.S.
PRESIDENT, ST. LUKE'S HOSPITAL, 1751-1790.

PLATE VI

ST. LUKE'S HOSPITAL

ROWLANDSON & PUGIN

FROM THE MICROCOSM OF LONDON

PLATE VII

ST. LUKE'S HOSPITAL
VIEW FROM THE SOUTH-EAST

PLATE VIII

WOODSIDE HOSPITAL, MUSWELL HILL

THE WEST WING.

who were bound to have varying views and be interested in different matters. This is well recognised in institutions and services which are regularly inspected and where the idiosyncrasies of the inspecting officers are, as a rule, carefully studied beforehand.

On the other hand the Visitors' Book, kept between 1829 and 1891, and then unfortunately allowed to fall into disuse, was full of enthusiastic remarks.

Charles Dickens, who it will be remembered, had visited St. Luke's for the Christmas Tree party in January 1852 and who was always keenly interested in the hospital, wrote on the 15th January, 1858: "Much delighted with the great improvements in the hospital under many difficulties, and with the excellent demeanour of the attendants, and with the benignant and wise spirit of the whole administration."

Visitors came to St. Luke's not only from every part of the United Kingdom, but from many European countries and the United States of America. Appreciations were in many languages of varying legibility with signatures that were generally illegible.

A contrast was the boldly written entry over the signature of Catherine Gladstone, in 1868. She wrote: "I am greatly struck and surprised. Everything seems admirably managed. The cheerfulness is not the least thing and very remarkable." Though her compliments were perhaps back-handed, her impressions were satisfactory.

Even allowing for the fact that most of these visitors could not have seen everything, the unanimity of their praise was remarkable. Many of them came from, and were in charge of, similar institutions elsewhere, and must have known what particular points were worth careful examination. Their wish to visit St. Luke's was testimony to the almost world-wide reputation of the hospital.

The Commissioners continued to press for more open air for the patients. They noted the improvement of the old burial ground, now turfed and laid out as a flower garden, but they pressed the Committee to buy a large vehicle and a pair of horses, so that eight or ten patients at a time might be taken for drives. They continued to hope, rather than to urge, for the establishment of a country branch.

In 1871 there seemed a chance of doing even more than this,

for the Treasurer received a letter from Mr. Swanston, Q.C., in which he offered to provide St. Luke's with a site of at least 20 acres on his estate near Leatherhead. It was "on high ground with beautiful views and conveniently situated near two stations on the South Western and Brighton lines respectively". His proposal was a complicated one, for the new hospital was to be built by him, but paid for by St. Luke's out of funds raised by public subscription and when completed was to be conveyed to St. Bartholomew's Hospital in exchange for part of the existing building and site in Old Street. (The other part would go to Mr. Swanston.) St. Bartholomew's could then convey the new building and the Leatherhead site on a perpetual lease to St. Luke's at a nominal rent in exchange for the present lease.

Mr. Swanston pointed out that the advantages of this scheme would be:

(1) St. Luke's would get a country site and the Charity would be relieved of the present rent and high rates and taxes.

(2) St. Bartholomew's would get as much of the Old Street site as would not be conveyed to Mr. Swanston, and on that would get a higher rent than what St. Luke's paid them.

He was willing to let St. Luke's have 20 acres or more, either at £200 an acre or in exchange for part of the Old Street site and building.

To meet the cost of the new hospital, Mr. Swanston suggested an appeal to the public. If this did not bring in enough, he thought that perhaps St. Bartholomew's might lend the balance; if not, it could be raised on mortgage, or he would be willing himself to lend the money in return for a larger proportion of the Old Street site.

Mr. Swanston never had any personal interview with the Treasurer or the Committee, but sent his architect and agent to explain the details to them, and after what seems to have been a very brief consideration, the Governors decided not to follow up the proposal. There is nothing in the minutes to suggest that anyone visited the proposed site or that there was any consultation with the Governing Body of St. Bartholomew's. The whole project was discussed and rejected in a month. Mr. Swanston's first letter was dated the 12th April; it came before the Committee on the 28th of that month, and was rejected on the 12th May.

The proposed site was admirable in all respects although the scheme may not have been practicable. It was not even mentioned in the Annual Report and there is no indication that the Commissioners, who would almost certainly have favoured it in principle, knew anything about it. Whether the proposed exchanges of sites and leases were practicable or would have served as a basis of discussion with St. Bartholomew's there is no means of guessing.

Possibly the cautious Committee thought the plan over-ingenious. The emphasis Mr. Swanston had laid on not wishing for any personal advantage may have made them suspicious. They may have discovered, after making enquiries, that under the disguise of a charitable and public-spirited wish to help the hospital, was a shrewd and far-seeing speculation in real estate. Or they may have felt that the financial risk was too great and this, coupled with a conservative affection for the old building, which was now so greatly improved, and to the central position to which they attached so much importance, may have determined them to stay where they were. But there is no evidence to prove or disprove these conjectures.

As a result of this proposal however, a Sub-Committee was appointed to discover what would be the position if St. Luke's gave up the Old Street site. In the first instance they consulted the architect of St. Bartholomew's. He wrote that his personal opinion was that the Governing Body of that hospital would neither buy a fresh site, nor put up and lease a new building for St. Luke's. In short he did not expect them to be particularly helpful or co-operative.

As regards the present value of the site or the building, he advised the Sub-Committee to get an expert opinion. Incidentally he showed them his plan for laying out the land if St. Bartholomew's obtained possession of it, so it is clear that he had considered the possibility of St. Luke's moving from Old Street.

It was thought that the subject was sufficiently important to go to the expense of a valuation by an expert and Mr. Clark of Farebrother Clark & Co. was consulted. His report was to the effect that the terms of the lease were such that the value of the building and site would be small, and that to demolish such a large building and rebuild with shops and small houses in such an inferior neighbourhood would be expensive and useless. It might, however, be used as another hospital, an almshouse, a brewery or some such institution.

Assuming agreement with St. Bartholomew's, Mr. Clark thought that the maximum that might be obtained for the freehold would be about £45,000. Of that he thought St. Luke's might claim £35,000 and St. Bartholomew's the remainder. This, however, was on the assumption that the two charities acted together "with a view especially to benefit St. Luke's Hospital".

On this very cautious report it was resolved that, if a satisfactory agreement could be made with St. Bartholomew's, it was expedient that St. Luke's be re-established elsewhere and the matter was referred back to the Sub-Committee with instructions to confer with the authorities of St. Bartholomew's.

There is no mention, however, of any approach to St. Bartholomew's at that period, and nothing to show whether the Sub-Committee met with a blank and uncompromising refusal or merely with an unhelpful attitude.

It is clear that the desirability of a move into the country or the establishment of a country branch remained in the minds of the Committee. The Commissioners, in any case, did not let them forget what they thought about the matter, and in March 1887 they suggested a plan which had reached them through one of the Governors of St. Luke's. Reminding the Committee that their objections to the building and its site in Old Street were as strong as ever, they wrote that they had ceased to press this subject for some years as they realised the difficulty of removing St. Luke's elsewhere. Now, however, they thought that there was an opportunity for overcoming that difficulty. They had heard that the Governing body of Dulwich College would shortly require a site for a school for the parishes of St. Luke's, Old Street, and St. Botolph, and at the same time had land at Dulwich which might prove suitable for a Lunatic Asylum. The Commissioners thought that possibly an exchange of the St. Luke's and the Dulwich site might be effected provided that:

(1) The authorities of Dulwich College had no objection to the establishment of a Lunatic Asylum in their neighbourhood;

(2) This Dulwich site was satisfactory to the Committee of St. Luke's, and the St. Luke's site suited the requirements of Dulwich College;

(3) Such terms could be offered to the Governors of St. Bartholomew's Hospital as would induce them to give their assistance in carrying out this scheme.

The Commissioners wrote that they fully recognised the difficulties that would have to be overcome, but thought the scheme worth consideration and implied that they would assist as far as they could.

The Committee, having considered this scheme and having presumably explored its possibilities, wrote two months later that they had regretfully come to the conclusion that, in view of the surrounding difficulties such as the extreme desirability of a central situation which would be lost to St. Luke's if the hospital were moved to Dulwich, and the inadequacy of the funds available for improvement, as distinguished from the capital fund entrusted to the Governors for the permanent maintenance of the Charity, they were unable at present to adopt the suggestions of the Commissioners.

It is difficult to avoid the conclusion that at this time the Committee or the majority of them were not very anxious to leave Old Street. The attention of the Commissioners had been drawn to the possibility of such an exchange by a member of the Committee, who was a resident in Dulwich. He at least must have been in favour of the exchange, but the majority was against him and wanted to continue improving the old building. Possibly also the Governing Body of St. Bartholomew's had been approached and were found to be exacting negotiators, and it is quite certain that St. Luke's Committee were hard bargainers. In subsequent pages will be found an account of the protracted negotiations which led finally to the sale of the hospital building and site.

Moreover, although the dividends derived from the General Fund and the fees received from patients now almost covered the annual cost of the hospital, the amount received in donations and legacies was fluctuating, irregular and generally small, while the annual subscriptions, apart from the Whitbread rent charge, were insignificant.

At that time charitable subscriptions seem to have been sent elsewhere, and in any case St. Luke's had never organised their appeals to the public with the efficiency and persistence of modern institutions. The large sums which they had spent on the hospital had not allowed them to build up the reserve that would be necessary if the main hospital were to be moved to a new site.

In 1880, the Committee, in their Annual Report, expressed the hope that they might soon be able to establish a small self-supporting convalescent home, for they believed that this would be of immense advantage to all the patients, and particularly to those discharged on the "trial" system in helping the process of recovery. This decision was a compromise. It could not benefit more than a small number of curable cases at a time and then only those who could afford to pay the fees necessary to make the establishment self-supporting. Its value would depend largely on the turnover of cases. It was, of course, better than nothing. The Committee, the Medical Officers and the Commissioners all believed that it would be of great value.

The first house suggested was Rustington Hall, near Littlehampton, but this apparently was not found satisfactory, and eventually it was decided to rent Nether Court at St. Lawrence-on-Sea, near Ramsgate. This was an old manor house standing in its own grounds of about 12 acres. It would accommodate about 15 or 16 patients and a domestic and nursing staff of 6 including a matron. A local general practitioner agreed to act as honorary consulting physician and the medical staff and members of the Committee of St. Luke's were to visit at regular and frequent intervals.

Nether Court was opened for female patients on the 17th July, 1893, when about £600 had been spent on furnishing it. From that time there was a fairly regular flow of patients and, after May 1905, of voluntary boarders. Despite the extra fee of 5s. a week paid by the patients, the expenses of Nether Court were heavy and it was never the self-supporting establishment that had been hoped, even when there were a certain number of voluntary boarders. These were patients admitted originally in 1905 at 3 to 5 guineas a week. They were supposed to stay for at least a fortnight and for not more than 3 months, but these rules seem to have been relaxed.

All the reports concerning this country branch were satisfactory and indeed enthusiastic. Both the patients and the nurses who were sent there in rotation, benefited from the bracing air of Ramsgate. The Commissioners also were pleased with the situation and the management of Nether Court, but regretted that the additional fee prevented the poorer patients from enjoying the advantages of the place. Each year the number of patients increased until the autumn of 1897, when it became necessary temporarily to close the home owing to an outbreak of scarlet fever. It was, however, reopened 6 months later.

The Medical Superintendent wrote that the Home had proved a convenient and satisfactory means of testing the stability of recovered patients before their discharge. The greater freedom that it was possible to allow them and the bicycle rides which had recently become so fashionable tended to stimulate their self-reliance and, when the time came for their discharge, they were found to have more confidence in themselves and, what was almost as important, their friends had more confidence in them.

In 1891 on the recommendation of the Commissioners, an assistant resident medical officer was appointed. The first holder of this post was Dr. William Rawes who continued in the service of St. Luke's Hospital until his death in 1916.

It was during the years 1891 to 1894 that considerable improvements were carried out in the interior of the hospital. Much was done, as has been told elsewhere, to give the male attendants and nurses better accommodation. The former were provided with a billiards room and the nurses were given a large and cheerful sitting room at one end of which they dined. The wards were made lighter and less gloomy by the removal of the old and obsolete windows and the substitution of iron sashes which let in more light and gave better ventilation. These alterations were made despite a considerable reduction in donations.

However, the income from the invested funds had increased slightly by re-investment. In 1892 Mr. Teesdale, solicitor to the hospital, raised this question with the Committee. He reminded them that under the Act of Incorporation (1 and 2,

Vic. Cap. 38) and the amendment to the Rules in 1851, the trustees were restricted in their choice of securities to the public funds of Great Britain and to stocks of which the interest was guaranteed by Parliament. Mr. Teesdale thought that these limited powers were extended by the Trust Investment Act of 1889 and this opinion being confirmed by counsel, he was instructed to apply to the Court for an order to this effect. When this was granted the Committee were to invest in railway debentures and other securities which gave a slightly higher rate of interest.

When the Rev. T. H. Cole resigned the Secretaryship in 1871 the appointments of Secretary and Chaplain were separated, and Mr. George Seymour was appointed Secretary. He held the post for four years when he and Dr. Eager, the Medical Superintendent, resigned in order to become the joint proprietors of a private asylum near Bristol.

Mr. Crespin then became Secretary, and when, in 1882, Mr. Walker retired on the death of his wife (the Walkers had served the hospital faithfully for 33 years) he was made Secretary-Steward with unhappy results, for in January 1884 the Treasurer had to call a special meeting of the General Committee to consider a letter from Mr. Crespin in which he stated that he found it necessary to resign "owing to long-standing financial difficulties", and stated "that the accounts would be found in order", he having only deducted the commission due to him on some that he himself had collected. However, the Committee took the precaution of calling for the duplicates of all receipts for the previous six months and appointed a firm of auditors to investigate matters. The Treasurer subsequently made a statement about their examination to the Committee and said that "matters were in the course of being filtered out". But what was caught in the filter was nowhere disclosed, though it is evident that Mr. Crespin's idea of the commission due to him was liberal.

These investigations resulted in a return to the old arrangement by which the offices of Secretary and Steward were separated.

Mr. Percy de Bathe, the son of the Treasurer, who had been most helpful in "filtering out" the accounts of the late Secretary-Steward, was elected Secretary, and Thomas Glover was appointed Steward.

Maintenance and repairs continued to be a heavy expense. From 1890 onwards the Committee in almost every annual report emphasised the heavy outlay they had been forced to make in order to bring the old building up to date, and begged the Governors to do what they could to increase subscriptions and donations. Year after year a number of the old heavy window frames were replaced by lighter and more modern sashes and each window, of which there seem to have been a great number, cost over £10.

Painting and distempering went on continually; all lavatories and bathrooms were completely reconstructed, cleaned and painted. A most serious operation was in connection with a sign of settlement in the East Wing. It was found that the foundations were being disturbed by a body of water in motion. Much had to be pumped away before pipes to carry off this water could be put down, but the result was satisfactory and there were no further signs of settlement. Not only were the wards and wings distempered and painted, but all the offices were dealt with likewise. The Committee took advantage of the expiration of the lease of a tenant to add a space 90 feet by 34 to the Airing Court for females. This involved the removal and rebuilding of more than 100 feet of the boundary wall.

Finally the whole of the exterior brick and stone work had to be repointed and repaired. This was a most costly business.

It was not surprising therefore that in 1903 the Committee reported that the General Fund had been depleted of £10,540 in the past 9 years.

Much, however, remained to be done. When funds were available they intended to remove at least 60 more of the old-fashioned window frames and to replace them with improved sashes. They wanted also to install electric light throughout the hospital and to have a modern heating plant as well, for there were still complaints both by the Commissioners and the Medical Officers that some parts of the hospital were very cold in winter.

The former reminded the Governors that the poorest members of the community were now treated in the County Asylums provided by the State. In consequence, during the past 50 years the patients in St. Luke's had been drawn from a higher grade, "i.e., our great middle-class population of limited means."

"This section of the community", they wrote, "is entitled to the generous sympathy and consideration of the Charitable Public; as a class they are educated persons, possessing refined feelings, pursuing definite vocations in life, with a recognised status to keep up, often on a very slender income. When it is fully realised that a mental illness, under any circumstances, is a most expensive business, as well as a trial to bear, it will be understood that in treating such patients, either gratis, or at a small contributory payment towards their maintenance, this Hospital is performing a necessary as well as a charitable duty."

At this time, i.e., from about 1894 to 1915, the weekly cost of maintaining a patient was just under 30s. a week and a very small proportion of the patients paid fees sufficient to cover this sum. Consequently it was only rarely that income exceeded expenditure, and when any improvements on the large scale, such as have been mentioned, were carried out it was necessary to encroach on the General Fund.

In 1905 this Fund had a book value of £162,660, and the average income from it was about £4,700, i.e., just under 3 per cent. It never reached £5,000 a year. This sum, together with donations, which tended to be fewer and smaller as time progressed, subscriptions, which were always insignificant, and the payments received for the maintenance of patients, made up the amount with which the Governors had to carry on their work.

This will explain—if explanation is needed—their scrupulous care in safeguarding their funds and the caution with which they embarked on any new schemes. That they were conservative and occasionally constrained by the influence of a long tradition is admitted, but of the honesty of purpose and absolute integrity of the long line of Governors, who, as Treasurers or members of committees administered St. Luke's, there can be no question.

An example of their fixed, indeed obstinate, determination to safeguard and preserve their funds in order to carry on in some form the work of the founders, is to be found in the negotiations which in 1916 culminated in the sale of the hospital and the Old Street site to the Bank of England.

VIII

NEGOTIATIONS FOR THE SALE OF THE HOSPITAL AND THE OLD STREET SITE

SOME account has already been given of proposals—in 1871 and 1887—to remove St. Luke's to another and better site in the country (see Chapter VII). These came to nothing, but it was clear that in such an event the attitude of St. Bartholomew's would be all important. Six years later in 1903 there began those long-drawn-out negotiations which continued for eleven years before, early in 1914, the two governing bodies were able to reach agreement over the division of the purchase money. Although the offer made in 1913 did not result in a sale, in the words of the General Committee "this important understanding greatly facilitated the business of selling the property" to the Bank of England in 1916.

It is thought that an abbreviated account of these negotiations is of sufficient interest to include in *The Story of St. Luke's Hospital*.

NEGOTIATIONS WITH ST. BARTHOLOMEW'S IN 1901-1909

On the 24th April, 1903, the hospital was visited by the Lord Mayor, Sir Marcus Samuel and the Sheriffs of London, Sir George Truscott and Sir Thomas Brooke-Kitching. After the Treasurer had given them a short history of the hospital, they inspected the wards and other parts of the building. The Lord Mayor told the Committee that he thought they had done most magnificent work with the building at their disposal, work which compelled his warm admiration. He felt, nevertheless, that they would be prudent and business-like if they did their utmost to come to an understanding with their landlord, so that eventually they could move the hospital into the country. He was sorry that they had not been able to accept the proposals which he made informally to amalgamate with the City of London Asylum, for he felt that sooner or later either the Charity or the Lunacy Commissioners might compel the removal of St.

Luke's from its present position. His Lordship concluded by saying that successful as St. Luke's was in the matter of cures, he thought their results would be even better if the institution were in the country. Thanking the Committee for their courtesy, he said he was proud of the fact that he was the first Lord Mayor to inspect St. Luke's Hospital.

Alderman Sir George Truscott also congratulated the Governors on the admirable work they had done, but he agreed that more successful work could be carried out in the country. He concluded by saying that the Corporation of London would be glad to help them in the event of removal and that, under the aegis of the present Lord Mayor, this year would be particularly opportune for considering the matter.

The Treasurer, Mr. Powell, in reply, said that the Committee for some years past had tried to come to an understanding with St. Bartholomew's Hospital in regard to the lease. He pointed out that there were many financial difficulties to overcome before the removal of the hospital would be possible.

The Lord Mayor promised to act as intermediary, and the proceedings terminated.

When discussing the problem subsequently, the Committee agreed that they could not leave the present site, and the building on which so much had been spent, unless they were given adequate compensation. They had explained their views to the Committee of St. Bartholomew's more than a year previously, and when a letter from the Governors of that hospital, written in January 1902, stated definitely that at that time they could not entertain any proposal that would deprive them of their freehold interest in the site occupied by St. Luke's, the Committee felt that no further action was possible. They had, however, clarified their wants as far as St. Bartholomew's were concerned, and two alternatives had been suggested, namely that:

(a) St. Luke's should buy the freehold for £10,000, i.e., about 46 years purchase of the present rent, or

(b) St. Bartholomew's should buy them out for £120,000.

The first alternative would have enabled St. Luke's to have sold the site for the best price obtainable without the complication of any further negotiations with the other Charity.

The second would have given them the sum they needed to remove the hospital, to buy a new site, and there build a modern hospital.

Either alternative would have been a good bargain for St. Luke's and not a very bad one for St. Bartholomew's.

In May the diplomacy and skilful negotiation of the Lord Mayor had been so far successful that he was able to tell Mr. Powell that he was authorised by the authorities of St. Bartholomew's to say that they were willing to sell their interests in the site of St. Luke's Hospital.

At a meeting of the representatives of both hospitals, the Treasurer of St. Bartholomew's defined their requirements, namely:

(1) St. Bartholomew's would require as a fixed first charge the capitalised value of the present rent and fine calculated at $2\frac{1}{2}$ per cent.

(2) St. Bartholomew's would consent to the sale of the land at not less than £150,000, each hospital to receive one half of the proceeds.

(3) St. Bartholomew's would be prepared to consider an offer from St. Luke's (after condition No. 1 had been satisfied), it being understood that as freeholders they would expect a very considerable sum.

(4) It was suggested that St. Bartholomew's could find a suitable piece of land as part payment together with a sum of £50,000 if St. Luke's were willing to accept such a proposition.

The negotiating Sub-Committee of St. Luke's, having considered these proposals, recommended:

(1) That no offer for the lease or for St. Bartholomew's interest should be made.

(2) That an offer be made to accept a fixed sum for the surrender of the lease and site.

(3) As a basis for discussion they suggested that this fixed sum should be £120,000.

They had made enquiries regarding the cost of building a new hospital, which the Commissioners in Lunacy hoped would be near London (and therefore on an expensive site) but had not been able to get reliable figures. They thought that it would be wise to estimate on a cost of £600 per bed.

The Committee, having considered these recommendations, agreed that the sum to be asked for the surrender of the lease, etc., should be raised to £130,000, and a letter to this effect was sent to St. Bartholomew's.

To this, St. Bartholomew's replied that, since in their opinion negotiations could only proceed on the basis of the interests of the two hospitals being of equal value, they could not modify their views and were entirely unable to accept the proposal of St. Luke's.

They suggested that, if negotiations were to continue, the practical step to be taken was to find out the value of the site. They proposed that this should be done by public auction or by tender.

The letter concluded by saying that St. Bartholomew's might be able to offer St. Luke's a site at Stanmore in Middlesex, on such reasonable terms as might facilitate the transaction.

To this the Committee replied briefly that no plan would meet their approval unless it guaranteed that St. Luke's Hospital for 200 patients could be reinstated in the country free of cost. They did not look for profit; all they wanted was a new hospital.

In reply, St. Bartholomew's wrote that they could only regard St. Luke's letter as putting an end to all negotiations. But St. Luke's were not willing that this should be the last word. They wrote on the 16th September, 1903, that they were sorry that their proposals had not been more favourably received. They considered that the terms laid down by St. Bartholomew's were not equitable in that they made the interests of that hospital superior to those of St. Luke's whose acceptance of them would have very materially curtailed their own efficiency. It remained only for them to submit the correspondence to their Governors in order to make the position clear to all, and also to correct an erroneous opinion currently held that they were mainly responsible for keeping the hospital in its present site and in so doing had prevented St. Bartholomew's from obtaining an increased income from the valuable site.

In acknowledging this letter the Treasurer and Almoner of

St. Bartholomew's expressed their regret that St. Luke's should not think them ready to come to an equitable arrangement. They still thought that their proposals were fair and were unwilling that negotiations should be closed without St. Luke's having had an opportunity of freeing themselves from their covenant, and were prepared to consider any reasonable offer to that end. They added that St. Bartholomew's were in no way responsible for the opinion which was said to be commonly held regarding the action of the Committee of St. Luke's.

In December 1903 the land agents and valuers consulted by St. Luke's in a long report stated that as a building estate they considered the St. Luke's site worth a gross rental of £4,462 and at 23 years purchase its capital value with certain deductions for development would be £101,672.

They calculated that the capital value to St. Bartholomew's, based on the existing rent and fine, was £7,275.

On this, the Committee of St. Luke's informed St. Bartholomew's that the latter's estimate of £150,000 was much in excess of the commercial value of the site, and suggested a conference between their valuer and the surveyor of St. Bartholomew's. The Treasurer and Almoners replied that while they were most anxious to bring these negotiations to a satisfactory conclusion, they thought that at present such a conference would not be of any advantage, but that if they might see the valuers' report they would give it most careful consideration. After examining this report they wrote that their surveyor considered the freehold value of the site to be £112,000 and renewed their assurance that they were ready to consider any reasonable offer by St. Luke's for the freehold.

It was decided that the two Treasurers should confer, but there is no record of such a conference, and for the time being the matter dropped.

In January 1906 a Special General Committee was called to consider whether an agreement could be reached regarding the division of the sum paid for the sale of the hospital, and site if, as was reported, there were a purchaser.

The Treasurer was authorised to negotiate with St. Bartholomew's on the following lines:

(1) As a first charge that £60,000 be guaranteed to St. Luke's as a minimum.

(2) As a second charge that £8,000 be then secured to St. Bartholomew's.

(3) These two amounts having been deducted from the sum realised by the sale, the balance to be divided equally between the two hospitals. A reserve of £120,000 to be placed on the property.

An amendment to this resolution omitted the proviso guaranteeing St. Bartholomew's £8,000 as a second charge. The minutes do not say whether this was carried.

On further consideration later in the month it was decided that the Committee was prepared to surrender their lease for £95,000. A letter to this effect was written to the Treasurer of St. Bartholomew's who replied that he and the Almoners considered that it was not possible to determine the sum that should be paid to St. Luke's until a definite offer had been made.

The Committee then decided to make an offer of £15,000 for the purchase of the ground rent and fine.

The answer of the Treasurer of St. Bartholomew's dated the 26th February, 1906, was to the following effect. Having recapitulated the terms of the lease he continued:

"You will readily understand, under these circumstances, it is very difficult for the advisers of St. Bartholomew's Hospital to put a figure on the value of our hospital's interest. I should not be prepared, as Treasurer of St. Bartholomew's, to permit St. Luke's Hospital (with your consent) to be put up to auction at St. Bartholomew's expense.

"The only kind of negotiation that is possible is that, if we were offered a definite figure, we (i.e., St. Bartholomew's and St. Luke's) should then endeavour to arrange what portion of that price each should receive.

"(signed) Ludlow, *Treasurer*."

To this St. Luke's replied that their letter offering £15,000 for the purchase of the lease, etc., had not been acknowledged, and in their opinion negotiations could not be conducted with reasonable prospects of success on the lines suggested in the last paragraph of Lord Ludlow's letter.

Lord Ludlow replied briefly that this was the only course he was prepared to accept.

On this ultimatum St. Luke's decided to seek advice from Counsel as to the possibility of taking powers to remove the hospital under a revision of the Incorporation Act of 1838.

In July 1907 Counsel gave his opinion which may be summarised as follows: he thought that a sale of their property could be made without the approval of the Charity Commissioners, but he advised the Corporation to apply to the Charity Commissioners for a scheme authorising the sale and the removal and building of a new hospital. As regards the relative advantages of a surrender of the lease or a purchase of the freehold reversion he thought that it would be safer to surrender the lease if St. Bartholomew's would pay them a proper sum in consideration of such surrender. But in his opinion, the best way would be for the two hospitals to concur in selling the hospital together, an arrangement being first made on proper evidence as to the proportions in which the purchase money should be divided.

For nearly two years there is no further mention of any negotiations until January 1909, when the Treasurer reported that he had been sounded regarding a proposal that the site of St. Luke's should be put up for auction with a reserve of £140,000. The Committee, however, still preferred the idea of buying the lease from St. Bartholomew's for £20,000.

In April of this year the Treasurer of St. Bartholomew's—now Lord Sandhurst—forwarded a copy of correspondence which he had had with the Charity Commissioners regarding the possible sale of the Old Street site. His letter recapitulated the terms of the lease, the unsuitability of the site for its present purpose, and the desire of the Committee of St. Luke's to establish a new hospital near London. He asked finally for the views of the Commissioners regarding the division of the proceeds and generally as to the rights of St. Luke's Hospital in the matter. The Commissioners having been satisfied that the original lease of 1776 was in order and had been subsequently confirmed by Act of Parliament in 1826, wrote that their considered opinion was that a sale was desirable in the interests of both hospitals, for St. Bartholomew's had no benefit from the increased value of the site while St. Luke's was tied to an unsuitable locality. As to the procedure and the value and share of the proceeds, the Commissioners would like to be advised by a surveyor of their own nomination.

Both hospitals were willing to have such a valuation, and St. Luke's were prepared to give all possible information, but they were not ready to pay a half share of the surveyors' fee of 500 guineas, as they considered they already had all necessary information. But they were prepared to pay 100 guineas. They renewed their offer to buy out St. Bartholomew's for £20,000, but as the other hospital wanted £49,000, negotiations again came temporarily to an end.

These negotiations had now gone on with little progress over a period of eight years. A reader of the minutes and correspondence must feel both admiration and exasperation. Admiration for the pertinacity—to put it mildly—with which both parties fought for the finances of their respective Charities; exasperation at the way in which they argued in a vacuum, or vulgarly speaking, at their attempts to divide the bear's skin before they had killed or even tried to kill the bear. Luckily for them, the bear grew fatter and his skin larger with every year that passed.

It never seems to have occurred to them to call an independent and unprejudiced arbitrator to settle the division of the purchase price. This had been suggested to St. Luke's by Counsel and by the Charity Commissioners to St. Bartholomew's, but both parties seemed convinced that they knew best what was fair and equitable at all events for themselves and so affairs dragged on at interminable length.

Without knowing the financial strength of St. Bartholomew's, only one side of the question is visible. There is no doubt that St. Luke's, assuming it was intended to build a new hospital of 200 beds, needed every penny they could get. Their donations were diminishing, their annual subscriptions were insignificant. The dividends derived from their general fund and patients' fees were barely enough to maintain the hospital. They were not enough to meet the constant structural additions and alterations necessary in an out-of-date and 120-year-old building, which, sooner or later would have eaten up the general fund.

In a letter dated 31st October, 1913, Messrs. A. & F. Gee & Son offered £135,000 for the freehold property, including all buildings and fittings, subject to their being given the sole option for about six months. In addition they were prepared to give a further £2,000 for the old Burial Ground.

On this the Committee decided to approach St. Bartholomew's and ask their consent to the suggested sale on the basis of £100,000 to St. Luke's and £35,000 to St. Bartholomew's, and the Secretary was instructed to write to St. Bartholomew's on these lines.

But St. Bartholomew's were not at all satisfied with this proposal. While agreeing to the sale they found the suggested division of the purchase price quite unacceptable and they adhered firmly to their original view that out of the price St. Bartholomew's should first receive a sufficient amount in Consols to yield the present rent and fine and that the balance should be divided three-fifths to St. Luke's and two-fifths to St. Bartholomew's, and they calculated that on this basis they should receive not £35,000 but £52,900. Further they pointed out that they had never recognised the complete reinstatement of St. Luke's as an essential element in the division.

The General Committee replied that such a division could not be accepted by them and that in any negotiations the reinstatement of St. Luke's was essential and ended by pointing out the urgency of reaching an agreement on this very favourable opportunity.

As a result of an interview between the Treasurer, St. Luke's, and the Estates Clerk, St. Bartholomew's, a further letter was sent to the latter hospital stating that St. Luke's would accept £95,000 and suggesting a reference to the Charity Commissioners for an opinion.

The next move was a meeting of the two Treasurers at which it was stated that St. Bartholomew's would accept £45,000 and pay one third of the expenses. After a meeting of the General Committee a letter was written offering £43,500, provided St. Bartholomew's paid all the expenses of the sale. This was accepted by St. Bartholomew's but the Treasurer and Almoners protested against having to pay the whole of the commission in addition.

Finally it was agreed that £135,000 should be accepted and that subject to the consent of the Charity Commissioners the division should be £92,000 to St. Luke's and £43,000 to St. Bartholomew's, the latter hospital to bear the amount of the commission (£1,350) as well as the legal and other expenses of the sale.

As already mentioned the offer of Messrs. Gee was not followed up and the firm relinquished their option early in 1914, but at last agreement had been reached between the two hospitals, and, when two years later the Bank of England offered to buy the building and the site, the offer was accepted without further discussion.

As soon as it became clear that the sale would take place no further applications for admission were accepted, and the numbers in St. Luke's were gradually reduced. All remaining in the hospital at the end of 1916 were either discharged to their homes or transferred to other institutions. These moves were carried out successfully despite severe winter weather in December 1916 and the beginning of 1917. The last patients left early in February of that year.

In their final report the Committee wrote:

"Notwithstanding the rather depressing external conditions, the interior (of the hospital) was very different, with spacious lofty wards, comfortably furnished and cheerfully decorated. Scarcely a year had passed without improvements having been carried out."

The last report on the old hospital of the Board of Control[1] contained these remarks:

"This Hospital (St. Luke's) has taken a very prominent part in the Lunacy administration of the country, having been established by voluntary subscription in 1751. . . . The gradual growth of a huge city up to its very doors had, of course, in many respects, made it unfit for its purpose, but until closed it had discharged valuable functions as a curative hospital, and, by receiving patients of a suitable class at low rates of payment, had taken a conspicuous share in real philanthropic work."

The story of this old hospital may well be closed with this record of the patients who had been received there.

Since the 30th July, 1751, the day on which the hospital was opened for the reception of patients, up to the 3rd February,

---

[1] The Commissioners in Lunacy had been reorganised as the Board of Control in 1913.

1917, the day on which the last of the patients left the hospital, 25,569 patients had been admitted. Of these

11,077 or 43.33 per cent. were discharged cured.
 5,205 ,, 20.36   ,,   ,,   ,,   ,,   relieved.
 6,744 ,, 26.37   ,,   ,,   ,,   ,,   not improved.
 2,543 ,, 9.94   ,,   ,,   had died.

The building suffered little damage during the war. In September 1915, during a German airship raid, an un-exploded shell from an A.A. gun fell on a bedroom in the south front of the building. In this room were a sick patient and a male nurse, but happily no one was hurt and little damage was done.

After the hospital had been closed, a bomb from a German airship fell on the roof of what had been the female division and penetrated the two upper floors to the ground floor. Had there been any patients in the hospital the loss of life would have been considerable, but at the time the building was in the hands of the contractors.

IX

TREATMENT, NURSING, ADMINISTRATION AND SOME CASES IN OLD STREET

THE records unfortunately give few details about the duties or training of the nursing staff at St. Luke's. When the hospital was founded, nursing, and especially mental nursing, was still in the dark ages between the end of the time when the religious orders cared for the sick and the reforms of the nineteenth century. In the eighteenth century it was not a profession for educated men or women, and too often it was not possible even to get persons of good character to look after the insane. The practice and methods at St. Luke's undoubtedly did something to raise the standard of mental nursing in England. This was due firstly to the determination of the founders, as evidenced by their original rules and regulations, not to allow at their new hospital any of the more flagrant abuses of other institutions, and secondly to their careful choice of their chief attendants, male and female.

For 65 years, with a very brief interlude, two couples, Joseph and Mary Mansfield followed by Thomas and Mrs. Dunston, were largely responsible for administration and nursing at St. Luke's. Doubtless the eminent visiting physicians settled all major points and had great influence on the staff, but they were not resident and not even daily visitors, while the resident apothecaries had not in those days the influence, the status or possibly the knowledge, of those experienced couples.

When the hospital was first opened, the staff consisted of the visiting physician, who came there probably twice a week, a surgeon, who came when necessary, the Resident Apothecary, the two head keepers, male and female, and two male and two female attendants. This staff did everything; treatment, nursing, housekeeping, catering, house-cleaning and cooking for 70 patients. They probably got some help from the more amenable patients.

The head keeper and his wife received £56 a year between them, and the attendant £14 a year. There was some increase in numbers but little in wages until 1789, when the hospital was established in the new building. The staff then consisted of the Master (£60), the Matron (£40), the Matron's Assistant (£25), a porter, a carver and three male keepers (all at £20), a cook, four gallery maids (nurses), two laundry maids and two house-maids (all at £16). The number of patients was then 210. The medical staff was unchanged. It is obvious, therefore, that patients can have had little individual attention save in exceptional circumstances.

The wages, which were paid half-yearly, were apparently fairly liberal for those early days, and the staff were well fed and probably as well housed as most domestic staff of that time. About 1809, however, Mr. Dunston reported that it had become very difficult to get "proper persons to do the service of the house". The Committee then raised some of the men's wages from £21 to £25, and some of the women's from £18 to £20 a year according to their length of service.

The staff was increased to 10 women and 6 men for 279 patients in 1821, and to 12 women and 9 men for 235 patients in 1829. In that year a second physician was appointed.

A few of the attendants may have had some previous experience, but it is safe to assume that the majority were chosen for personal rather than professional qualifications. Experienced persons like the Mansfields, the Dunstons and their successors would probably have a good idea who, among the applicants for service, had natural aptitude for nursing, which is the most important of all qualifications, although it is, of course, fortified by training. Many of them could not even sign their names, but that is hardly surprising in view of the general standard of education in the eighteenth and early nineteenth centuries. In all cases the staff were engaged on probation in the first instance.

What is surprising is the proportion of patients who were cured and how frequent were entries in the minutes of the House Committee to the effect that "the Physician having reported that a patient admitted on ——— is cured of his Lunacy, and he, being called in and returning thanks, the Committee ordered his discharge, the Sureties attending to take him away." It is also surprising, considering the class from which the attendants were drawn, that there were so few cases of ill-treatment. Any complaints on such grounds were investigated by the Committee and in later years by the Commissioners in Lunacy also. On the other hand there are records of violence towards the attendants by the patients. Jane Hughes, for instance, "who had been in the service of the hospital for 15 years, was struck on the breast by a patient" and was so bad that the Committee granted her £20 to go to the seaside to recover her health.

There were likewise occasions when the staff showed unselfish courage as when a patient set herself on fire and would probably have been burned to death had not one of the gallery maids "with great presence of mind and at the hazard of her life extinguished the flames, but not without burning herself considerably." The Committee rewarded her with a grant of two guineas.

In 1830 the long reign of Thomas Dunston came to an end. When his wife died in 1816 he had resigned the Mastership, but was persuaded by the Committee to remain on as Superintendent. He was succeeded by his understudy, William Stinton, whose wife Clementina became Matron. Of them more hereafter.

The first of the physicians' annual reports to the Governors of which there is a record was in 1829, by Dr. A. R. Sutherland. He urged the separation of patients into regular categories and recommended more frequent hot baths. He and his colleague, Dr. John Warburton, first mentioned occupation and amusement for the patients in 1833, and thereafter the importance of this aspect of treatment was urged almost every year either by the physicians or the Commissioners in Lunacy. Elizabeth Fry indeed had written even earlier (April 1831) that "it is very important to have the mind properly occupied and the attention engaged as far as it can be". But in this, as in other things, she was ahead of her time.

Dr. A. R. Sutherland, who resigned in 1841, was a physician of vast experience and had been a witness in almost every great law case of his time where lunacy was in question. He was one of the earliest advocates of tonic treatment for insanity, and he repudiated bleeding, purging and vomiting.

During the later years of Dr. A. R. Sutherland, the abolition of all restraint was being advocated in particular by Dr. Pinel in France, and Drs. Tuke, Gardiner Hill and Connolly, in this country. But belief in restraint died hard. Drs. A. R. Sutherland

and John Warburton in 1840 gave a solemn warning against the risks that might be run if it were entirely abolished.

In 1851, Drs. A. J. Sutherland, who had succeeded his father, and F. R. Philp made an important report in which they reviewed the medical work of the hospital during the past 100 years, and gave fuller details about treatment than is recorded elsewhere.

They outlined the treatment of the three earliest physicians, Drs. Battie, Brooke and Simmons (1750-1811). Something is known of Dr. Battie's methods and theories from his writings (see pp. 17, 18). Both he and Dr. Brooke appear to have been believers in medical rather than moral treatment. But it is certain that there was considerable restraint and severity at St. Luke's in their time. Receipted bills for handcuffs and leg logs are in existence, and the cold plunge bath (made at a cost of £13) into which patients were thrown was doubtless in frequent use. Indeed, it was not abolished for about 100 years. Owing to the very small number of attendants, restraint must have been a practical necessity.

Dr. Simmons (1781-1811) was said to be much harsher in his methods, which were criticised by implication in the centenary report where it was stated that the percentage of cures in 1791 and 1800 was much lower than in 1831-1840. Doubtless Thomas Dunston was influenced by Dr. Simmons when he said, according to Dr. Rawe's history, that he had never seen much advantage from medicines and that he relied on management. He had the power of ordering a patient into seclusion or of putting on manacles as a punishment when patients misbehaved, and he believed fear to be the most effectual principle by which to reduce the insane to orderly conduct. Otherwise he was a humane man who disliked the use of the strait waistcoat and preferred a light "chain which was more pleasant to the patient".

Although Dr. A. R. Sutherland did not believe that restraint could be entirely abolished it was during his time that it was carefully watched and the numbers under restraint were for the first time reported at the weekly meetings of the House Committee.

In the Centenary Report the writers began by reminding the Governors that the percentage of recoveries during

E   121

the past 30 years had been steadily increasing and were:

$$\text{From } 1821 \text{ to } 1830 \quad .. \quad .. \quad 47\tfrac{1}{3}$$
$$,, \quad 1831 \text{ ,, } 1840 \quad .. \quad .. \quad 56\tfrac{1}{4}$$
$$,, \quad 1841 \text{ ,, } 1850 \quad .. \quad .. \quad 60\tfrac{3}{5}$$

They went on to recapitulate the improvements recommended by them and carried out by the Committee during the previous ten years. They were as follows:

In 1841 infirmaries for male and female patients were established.

In 1842 a Chaplain was appointed and a chapel was fitted up. Open fire-places were built in the galleries, coercion was abolished, padded rooms were made, and a special airing ground for noisy patients was set apart. In the galleries wooden doors were substituted for the iron prison-like gates and wire guards were taken away from many of the windows.

In 1843 reading rooms were established and bagatelle and backgammon boards were provided.

In 1845 under the Lunacy Act the hospital came under the joint government of the Governors and the Commissioners in Lunacy. The physicians believed that this would be of benefit to the patients *provided there was mutual good understanding between the two governing bodies*.

In 1848 the chapel was improved by the presentation of an organ. Gas was introduced this year throughout the hospital.

In 1849 strict and searching investigation was made regarding ventilation, drainage and water supply when there was some fear of another cholera epidemic.

The report went on to review the treatment at St. Luke's and in view of its interest this is quoted *in extenso*.

THE MEDICAL TREATMENT

"When the Hospital was first opened, Dr. Battie was its physician; in his time, and in that of Dr. Thomas Brooke, his successor, six apothecaries supplied the medicines to the patients gratuitously. The medical treatment consisted principally in anti-spasmodic and purgatives, and the patients seem to have escaped the practice, at one time prevalent in the treatment of lunacy, of being bled and purged every spring and fall. But a time arrived when the Physician appointed to the hospital had no faith in medicine, but relied chiefly upon moral treatment, upon good diet and exercise and upon the occasional use of purgatives for effecting a cure; and we find that the average percentage of recoveries during this period, i.e., from 1791 to 1800 was 11½ points lower than that between 1831 and 1840. This fact alone, without reference to any other considerations, would have convinced us of the importance of attending to the medical treatment of the patients confined to our care, and we are of opinion that the moral treatment being the same, and other things being assured equal, the number of re- coveries will advance *pari passu* with the improvement in our knowledge of the pathology and medical treatment of the disease.

"The medical treatment of insanity was not neglected by those who immediately preceded us. Dr. Warburton was the first physician in the country who prescribed morphia to allay the irritation of the nervous system and to procure sleep. This medicine has been considered by some a specific in all cases of insanity. In our opinion the choice of any remedy, more especially that of a sedative, is not un- important; opium, stramonium, belladonna, henbane, hemlock, ether, etc., have each their peculiar effect on the nervous system; and it is not even a matter of indifference whether opium or its salts are prescribed. If, therefore, we were to be reduced to the employment of one medicine only as a specific for all cases, we should consider that we were going back to those times when insanity was supposed to be cured by hellebore, or to the dark ages when it was treated by exorcism.

"In 1848 we took advantage of the assistance of Dr. Parker, who officiated in the absence of the resident medical officer, to ascertain the effect of the inhalation of ether and chloroform in the treatment of insanity . . . and we will give very briefly the conclusions we have arrived at upon this subject.

"(1) The same caution is requisite in the selection of patients in administering ether and chloroform, as in all other cases.

"(2) The inhalation of these substances arrests the

paroxysm of mania and sometimes procures sleep, but does not appear to have any curative influence upon the disease.

"(3) The only patients who have derived any decisive benefit from inhalation have been those labouring under acute dementia, when ether was prescribed as a stimulant.

"(4) Ether and chloroform, although beneficial in epilepsy are injurious in cases of epilepsy complicated with insanity.

"(5) One case only of puerperal mania has been admitted into the hospital after the inhalation of chloroform during parturition, and it is fair to state that the patient had had a previous attack after a former labour when chloroform was not administered.

"(6) The inhalation of ether and chloroform has been recommended where patients obstinately refuse their food. Our experience of the effect under such circumstances is very limited but not unsatisfactory.

PUPILS

"In 1753 a law was passed for the admission of pupils to the Hospital and Dr. Battie permitted medical men to observe his practice. In 1843 this law was revived and a course of Clinical Lectures is given annually at the Hospital to pupils who are selected by the Physicians of the Metropolitan Hospitals, and who are allowed to attend the Course gratuitously.

MORAL TREATMENT

"The moral treatment of our patients is based upon those benevolent principles which have been so humanely endeavoured to be carried out at other Asylums. We believe that the only question which can now arise is by what method the insane can be treated in the most humane manner. We should, however, be deceiving the profession and the public if we were to say that the result of our experience leads us to the belief that restraint can be abolished with advantage in all cases and under all circumstances. But in saying this we distinctly repudiate the notion of encouraging by our example any return to the cruel method of treatment formerly practised; and we assert that we feel no sympathy with those who employ restraint merely for the purpose of saving trouble to themselves and attendants. There is no general rule without its exceptions, and we conscientiously think that there are some exceptions to the total abolition of coercion. ... The exceptions to our general rule of the non-employment of coercion in the Hospital amount to 2 in 100.

"The chief burden of the moral treatment falls upon the resident officers of the establishment; and we take this opportunity of thanking them for carrying out our wishes with so much zeal and discretion. . . . It is very gratifying to see the influence of occupation and amusement upon the minds of the patients. . . . Balls are given in the Hospital once a fortnight; the male and female patients meet in the centre corridor and we are glad to find that they not only enjoy themselves in singing and dancing, but that they also behave with the utmost decorum.

"But that which we consider to be the chief and most important part of the moral discipline of the Hospital is the daily attendance of the officers and of a certain number of the patients in the chapel, when a portion of the Liturgy is read, and where the practical duties of Christianity are taught by our worthy Chaplain."

The report can probably be accepted as the concise and considered opinion of two experienced physicians on the treatment of insanity, so far as the conditions at St. Luke's and the state of medical knowledge then allowed.

In their report of 1853 they again urged the importance of occupation and amusement, and concluded with the statement that what was essential in the treatment of insanity consisted neither in the situation of the asylum and the magnificence of the building, nor in the occasional indulgence of the patients, but in uniform and consistent sympathy, in daily self-denial, in control of temper, mutual forbearance and Christian charity shown by the officers not only to the patients but to one another.

Restraint was entirely abolished and Seclusion substituted in 1856.

As already mentioned Thomas Dunston finally retired in 1830. William Stinton had already succeeded him as Master in 1823, and his wife Clementina was appointed Matron in 1826.

They held these posts until 1849 when Stinton wrote to the Committee as follows:

"Sir and Gentlemen,
"Deeply painful as it is to my feelings I am admonished (sic) that the period has arrived rendering it incumbent upon me to make known to you the desire of Mrs. Stinton and myself to withdraw from the service of your excellent Charity . . . I may perhaps be permitted to state the period we have been in the service of the Hospital, namely myself 26 years and Mrs. Stinton 23 years . . . and as evidence of my close attention to duty I hope I shall be forgiven in mentioning the fact that during such period I have been absent but one weekly (House) Committee day."

The Committee accepted the resignation with deep regret and recorded "their appreciation of the strict integrity and exemplary kindness combined with acknowledged competency", with which the Stintons had discharged their duties. They awarded them a joint pension of £100 a year and of £60 a year to whomever of them survived the other.

Thomas Collier Walker and his wife Clementina Eliza from Union House, Eastry, in Kent, succeeded the Stintons.

It was Mrs. Walker's "clear head and strong heart" that Charles Dickens praised so warmly in his article. On the other hand she and her husband were both criticised by Dr. Bucknill in the hypercritical paper, which he wrote, inspired by Dr. Stevens, the Apothecary at St. Luke's, in the *Journal of Mental Science*.

There had always been some tendency for friction to arise between the Steward and his wife on the one hand and the Resident Apothecary or Medical Superintendent on the other, for the conflicting claims of administration, nursing needs and medical demands were bound to clash until many years later when their interdependence in the interest of the patient was fully and intelligently recognised.

Mr. and Mrs. Walker remained at St. Luke's until 1882 when the latter died and the former retired. They were representatives of the best of the old school, but they belonged definitely to that school. In the 33 years during which they held office, there had been immense changes in the training and practice of nursing. Before the middle of the nineteenth century it was recognised in some quarters that better and more systematic training for general nursing was necessary. At first this recognition was reluctant and changes were small. But the tempo was greatly quickened by the ghastly failures to provide for the sick and wounded in the Crimean War, followed by the insistent and influential demands of Miss Florence Nightingale for better nursing and more efficient provision for the needs of the sick.

The *Story of St. Luke's* cannot do more than touch on the sometimes obstructed progress in these matters, but the hospital can hardly have been unaffected by it, although the Walkers would have been more than human had they been able to keep completely abreast of the times.

They were the last of the married couples to hold the positions of Master and Matron.

In many ways the hospital must have benefited by the long experience and gathered wisdom of a series of only four married couples to hold these important posts for 130 years, but it may have been that the long tradition of their faithful and efficient service, and the very fact that it was on the Master that the Committee always relied, that led the Governors so determinedly to oppose, even as late as 1906, the principle laid down by the Commissioners in Lunacy that the Resident Medical Superintendent (the lineal descendent of the Resident Apothecary) should, under the Committee, exercise entire control, administrative as well as medical, in the hospital.

During all these years the status and qualifications of the Apothecary had grown gradually higher. In 1823 the Committee decided that he should "take his seat with the other medical gentlemen of the establishment at the weekly meetings of the Committee".

In 1828 his duties were revised and he was instructed to report weekly to the Committee the numbers under restraint and the progress of patients. It was his duty also to keep the Case Book, giving an account of every patient.

But it was not until the hospital was visited by the Commissioners in Lunacy from 1845 onwards, and Dr. Bucknill's article in the asylum journal was published that matters first came to a head.

In this article it was stated that the Treasurer was practically a dictator, and that the Steward, not the Medical Superintendent, was the master of the hospital. This article was written in 1854. It included many other recommendations all inspired by Dr. Stevens and all incidentally very sound. Many of them were carried out subsequently.

It would seem that Dr. Stevens was an extremely able young man, a determined reformer and quite exceptionally tactless. During his stay at St. Luke's he did an immense amount of good but all concerned with the hospital must have breathed a sigh of relief when he left in 1860 after seven turbulent years.

Meanwhile, the Governors had revised their regulations, but they managed to leave some loopholes whereby the Matron and Steward evaded the control of the Resident Medical Superintendent which resulted in another and final clash between the Committee and the Commissioners some 50 years later.

After the Walkers, Stewards and Matrons, and from 1882, head male attendants, were appointed individually and nearly all had been trained at one of the great hospitals. The succession of married couples was no doubt advantageous for a time, but in the changing circumstances and more modern conditions that followed the reforms inspired by Florence Nightingale, independent and individual appointments were an improvement. Married couples are apt to support one another, right or wrong. Lengthy tenure of office, as a rule, does not make for progress or efficiency, for only exceptional individuals can maintain their initial velocity. Fresh blood and new brooms (if such a mixed metaphor is permissible) are not as a rule soothing, but the most disturbing and unpleasant of them generally do some good. The Matron who succeeded Mrs. Walker held her post for more than 21 years; the lady who followed her, who was clearly a determined individualist, caused considerable friction and made St. Luke's, as far as can be judged from the records, a thoroughly unhappy family. The Resident Medical Superintendent, Dr. Rawes, complained of her, and there was a considerable exodus of nurses, but the Committee, in supporting the Matron, pointed out that on her appointment she had found the state of the female staff unsatisfactory. They were re-drafting the regulations at the time, and had revised Matron's duties. She was in future to be the "Head Female Officer" and exclusively occupied with the wards, while the Head Laundress, the Needlewoman and the household servants were made subject to the Steward who, at that time, was also the Secretary. When Dr. Rawes renewed his complaints about the Matron's high-handed and independent action, the Committee repudiated "the baseless charges" against her, and insisted on her authority in all nursing and household matters. Far from supporting the Medical Superintendent's recommendation that she should go, they seriously considered the question of asking Dr. Rawes to leave.

Happily such a disaster (for a disaster it would have been), was averted. But not until the Commissioners had taken very strong action. They wrote pointing out that the revised regulations would have no force until they were sanctioned by the Secretary of State and that they would not be recommended for such sanction by the Commissioners so long as they infringed the principle that the whole control of the administration should, under the Committee, be exercised by the Medical Superintendent. They concluded by stating plainly that the Governors "appear to be under some misapprehension of their powers".

On this the Committee gave way, and Dr. Rawes held out an olive branch promising to do everything he could to restore harmony in the hospital. This was in 1908.

This was the last round in the long battle which had begun more than 50 years previously. Henceforward, St. Luke's seems to have been happy, and therefore efficient, under the rule of Dr. Rawes as long as it remained at Old Street.

It is necessary now to revert to the various steps taken to improve the nursing in St. Luke's.

In 1853 a Sub-Committee of Governors reported that a great improvement had taken place in the treatment of patients during the last 10 or 12 years, but that there must be constant supervision over the attendants of the insane to prevent any relapse into carelessness or ill-treatment. It was recommended that the senior attendant in each gallery should be allowed to keep a belt and gloves under lock and key, to be used only in cases of emergency. The gloves could be put on the patient and locked to the belt. They were a form of restraint. The medical officers did not approve of this treatment if it could be avoided, but sometimes "it was the only safe method of preventing disaster".

At this time, apparently, the Steward and the Matron were so fully occupied with administrative and domestic duties that Dr. Stevens had considered that as far as nursing duties were concerned they were unnecessary. The Committee did not agree with such a drastic change, but they were sufficiently impressed with Dr. Stevens' views as to appoint a head attendant or nurse to each ward, and they raised the probationer nurses initial salary to £16 rising to £20 after two years' service. They also improved their accommodation. The nursing staff did not wear uniform until many years later, but were required to wear a "decent" dress, for which, presumably, they were given a small allowance.

The Commissioners in 1857 considered the nurses of a superior order and better than the men. But none of the nursing staff were expected to have any special qualifications, though the authorities at St. Luke's gave preference to those with previous experience of mental nursing.

The medical officers stated plainly that something more than higher wages was required to raise the standard of the nursing staff in asylums and mental hospitals, the low standard and lack of qualifications of which had been deplored by Lord Shaftesbury when he raised the question in Parliament.

An improved standard became all the more necessary after 1856 when restraint was completely abolished in the hospital. Difficult patients were then put in seclusion for short periods and judging from the Commissioners' Reports such seclusion was usually very brief.

At St. Luke's the medical officers did what they could to improve the training of attendants and nurses, while the Committee improved the conditions under which they worked, freeing them of some of the drudgery of domestic work and giving them more free time. Whether their insistence in 1869 that all employees were to be members of the Church of England had any effect on their standard is doubtful, for the Commissioners still complained of the inferiority of the male nurses and wrote that the changes among them were so frequent that there was no time to train them. The miscellaneous duties of the Steward were so heavy that he could not have paid much attention to nursing and the Commissioners had to press for a head male attendant for 20 years before one was appointed in 1882. The Matron, on the other hand, from very early days, had an assistant, and this was probably partly the cause of the better nursing and higher standard in the female division. The first head male nurse was not a success and had to be discharged almost immediately, but thereafter there was a definite improvement in that division.

A major defect in the administration was that the supremacy of the Medical Superintendent had never been clearly or finally established. Consequently there was divided responsibility. Moreover the Committee still insisted that they must settle everything. They would not even give authority to the House Committee. This meant that, at the best, some questions were settled only at their monthly meetings, but very often delays were very much longer, particularly when the amateurs on the Committee did not agree with their advisers or when their advisers disagreed among themselves. For instance, a proper system of night duty raised by the Commissioners in 1862 was not approved until 1868. The appointment of a head male attendant was delayed even longer. It is extremely difficult to read between the lines of carefully and discreetly worded minutes, and "after full consideration" or "the question was deferred for further consideration" may or may not conceal the most violent disagreement resulting in the meeting being unable to make up its own mind.

The number of the nursing staff was gradually increased, but it is difficult to give exact numbers, as in the earlier years the numbers included cooks, needlewomen and domestic staff. The Commissioners reported that the staff was insufficient up to 1873, when the numbers were 8 male attendants and 13 nurses. In 1874, 3 probationer nurses and 1 male probationer were engaged. Their wages at this time were, for the men £27 10s., rising to £32 10s., and for the women, £18, rising to £24.

In 1879 the Commissioners were glad to report that short service was the exception, not the rule. In 1882 salaries were again raised for those with long service, and the number of the staff was 28. Thereafter it rose to an average of 34 until 1912 when the numbers fell during the first two years of the war until 1916 when the hospital was closed. The proportion of the staff with over 5 years' service averaged about 27 per cent. The Commissioners, during these years, reported well on the nursing.

In 1893 the Medical Superintendent reported that he was

not happy about the nurses' health. He considered this was due to their indifferent accommodation. They had no proper sitting room and some of them had to sleep in the wards. The Committee took immediate action; seven single bedrooms were added and a sitting room was provided. Both it and as many bedrooms as possible were to be away from the wards. From this time onward there were no more complaints about the nurses' accommodation, but, as long as St. Luke's remained in Old Street, there was no possibility of a separate Nurses' Home.

In 1893 the staff were put into uniform. At first the nurses were given an annual allowance of £2 and provided their own dress, but in 1904 the system was changed. All material was provided and became the property of the hospital. Uniform was worn only on duty and it included a cap, collar, cuffs and apron.

About 1890 certificates for proficiency in mental nursing were first issued by the Royal Medical Psychological Association, and in 1894 these were conferred on 4 attendants and 7 nurses who had been trained by Dr. Rawes. There is no further mention of these certificates until 1910 when 3 nurses passed the examination, and in 1913, when 4 nurses and 1 attendant passed the preliminary, and 4 nurses the final examination for this certificate.

In 1903 the issue of beer to the staff was discontinued and a monetary allowance was given to them instead.

In 1907 all employees were insured under the Workmen's Compensation Act.

In the same year each floor was supervised by a head nurse who was designated "Sister". This was the first mention of ward sisters in St. Luke's Hospital.

In 1905 the Committee decided, as an experiment, to start a private nursing department, the object of which was to supply trained mental nurses to the public. It was to be under the Matron and separate from the ward staff. The experiment started with two certified nurses who were to be paid £30 a year with uniform and with a commission of not more than 10 per cent. on their earnings. This proved a success, and in 1907 twelve nurses were employed on private nursing, and it was agreed that the number should be increased. In 1915 the scheme was put on a more regular footing, and an independent matron was put in charge of this department.

With regard to treatment, the records and reports become increasingly statistical and decreasingly interesting as time passed. There is, therefore, little evidence of the methods practised, but the general remarks of the physicians and their accounts of some of the more unusual cases that passed through their hands are perhaps worthy of record.

They continued to complain that, owing largely to the difficulties and delays in obtaining the necessary certificates, many patients arrived in a late stage of their illness, often in a critically weak condition. This made it difficult to do anything for them and also increased the expenses of the hospital as they had to be given special diet and stimulants.

They found it interesting to observe, though melancholy to record, that nearly a third, and sometimes more, of the patients had a history of hereditary predisposition. The chief exciting causes were worry, mental anxiety, domestic troubles or adverse circumstances. Generally speaking, they did not think that cases were due to excessive alcoholism, nor did they seem, like earlier medical officers, to attribute insanity to malnutrition in early life.

Most cases, they wrote, were admitted during the summer, or the disease had begun in that season.

It was a constant cause of complaint that the ignorance of relations and friends led to the removal of patients who might have been cured in time, for there had been remarkable recoveries after prolonged treatment; some patients had been discharged cured after eleven and even fourteen years in the hospital. On the other hand, one patient died, aged 96, having spent forty years in St. Luke's.

They admitted that it was extremely difficult in some cases to determine either the existence of or complete recovery from insanity, and gave as an example the case of a man who recovered sufficiently to be sent home, and who went on trial for three months and then hanged himself, having given no sign of a suicidal tendency.

They found that despite the introduction of new remedies, including probably many of value, there was no appreciable increase in the proportion of recoveries during recent years. On the other hand the statistical tables which they prepared did not tell all the benefits which patients got from a stay in St. Luke's. A number of them, they considered, probably became insane owing to want of any training or any discipline during their lives. Such persons, even of mature age, benefited so much from the regular system, the discipline and the care taken of them in hospital, that many of them gained enough self-control to make it possible for their friends or relations to look after and manage them.

Some remarkable cases both of cure and relapse are recorded in these reports. A woman aged 41 was admitted suffering from restless melancholia, having been under care for five years. For six more years there was no change in her condition. Then she began to improve mentally and in general health. Six months later she was discharged bright, cheerful and energetic, and apparently capable of taking care of herself in every way.

Another unusual case was a man who, when admitted, was suffering from melancholia with some symptoms suggesting general paralysis. After three months' treatment these symptoms disappeared and he was discharged. For two years he was apparently perfectly well, but he then came voluntarily to the hospital and insisted on admittance, as he was "hearing voices and knew himself to be dangerous". He passed rapidly through all the stages of general paralysis and died five months later.

A patient who made a surprising recovery was a man admitted suffering from acute mania. He passed quickly into a state of stupor and remained in this condition with little change for five years. During that time every known remedy had been tried and all hope of his recovery had been given up. At the end of this time he began gradually to show signs of intelligence, then to take an interest in his surroundings and finally to improve so rapidly that he was given leave of absence and eventually was discharged in better health than he had enjoyed for many years, and able to carry out his duties in the service of his former employers.

It is regrettable that among the many statistical tables attached to these reports there are no detailed descriptions of treatment and remedies that were successful. These would have been of equal interest whether considered technically, generally or historically.

X

ST. LUKE'S CONVALESCENT HOMES

THE first convalescent home at Nether Court, near Ramsgate, has already been mentioned. It was rented from 1893 until January 1901 when the property was bought by St. Luke's for £3,600.

It was in use until July 1915 when it was lent to the Kent Voluntary Aid Detachment of the Red Cross as an auxiliary hospital for men of the services during the First World War. Extra buildings were put up to enable the admission of 90 patients, and it continued to be used as a service hospital until early in 1918 when it was closed owing to persistent bombing.

When St. Luke's Hospital was closed in 1916, Nether Court was let until 1923, when it was sold.

It was doubtless the success of Nether Court, coupled with its inadequate accommodation and the fact that only female patients could be sent there, that influenced the Governors in their decision in 1910 to buy Welders House and estate in Buckinghamshire.

But it was not merely as a convalescent home in the country that Welders House and estate of 100 acres and Jordans Farm of about 35 acres on the borders of the Chiltern Hills were bought. The Committee definitely intended to extend there the work of St. Luke's, and they probably hoped that on this considerable acreage it would some day be possible to build a third St. Luke's Hospital. It had long been their intention, if a suitable area of land could be obtained in a healthy situation about 20 miles from London, gradually to establish there a branch of the hospital. Patients would have the advantage of fresh air and a country life, and at that distance from London it was believed that the medical officers could visit them more often than had been possible at Nether Court.

Such a situation was found at Welders, of which St. Luke's was given possession in February 1910. The purchase was effected by borrowing £15,000 from the bank.

Welders is a substantially built modern house in good order, and needing little alteration to make it suitable for patients. It could hold about the same number as Nether Court. But it had the same disadvantage, namely that there was no separate accommodation for the nursing or domestic staff.

The situation and site were admirable. The house, standing some 300 feet above sea level, faced south, and had wide views in that direction, while it was sheltered by gently rising ground and trees to the north. The gardens were well laid out and there were pleasant walks, including a road within the estate from the house to the East Lodge. These walks could be easily extended inside the estate, which was well wooded, particularly with beeches, characteristic of that part of England. There was also a good kitchen garden and a fair orchard.

Jordans Farm of nearly 35 acres lies to the north of Welders on the other side of Welders Lane, which for about a mile forms the north boundary of Welders Estate. At that time 10 acres of the farm were arable and the remaining 25 were meadows with a good cherry orchard. It was the intention of the Committee to use this land for the production of vegetables, fruit, poultry, and eggs, both for the new branch and for the hospital, for it had better soil than the main estate where the land is poor, more fitted for forestry—or building—than for farming.

The old farm-house was then in a dilapidated condition and the Committee decided to repair it carefully, for it was of historical interest having been used as one of the earliest meeting houses of the Quakers since soon after the formation of the Society of Friends in the middle of the seventeenth century. In 1671 William Russell of Jordans Farm sold a portion of his land to the Society as a burial ground, and in 1688 his son sold them another 4 acres. It was on this land that the well known meeting house "Jordans" was built, and in the burial ground are the graves of William Penn and other distinguished Quakers.

The Committee hoped that the old farm-house might be made habitable at moderate expense, but soon found that it was in such bad condition that extensive repairs were necessary and urgent. New foundations had to be built on three sides, portions of the external walls restored and ceilings and floors had to be repaired. It may have been a relief when they were approached by the Society of Friends and asked if they would sell the house and 7 acres. The sale was completed before the end of 1911.

Six years later the house at the east end of the property, Welders Orchard, with 11¾ acres and another field of 6¾ acres, were bought. In 1920, 5 acres of Welders Wood were also added to the property.

The only structural alterations to the house that were necessary were two interior smoke screens and an exterior iron staircase as precautions in case of fire. A hand-power laundry was fitted up in a hut near the house. The walled kitchen-garden was well cultivated as were also two fields of Jordans Farm, and not only was Welders supplied with fruit and vegetables, but produce to the value of about £250 was sent each year to the hospital in London.

Until, however, extensions could be built, Welders could accommodate only the same number of patients as Nether Court, and such a small hospital must be relatively most expensive to maintain. Moreover, a converted private house is bound to be inconvenient. For instance, separate staff accommodation is particularly essential in hospitals for mental or nervous cases, and is now recognised as most desirable in all hospitals.

Another disadvantage of the place was—and is—its isolation and lack of communications. The nearest railway stations were then Gerrards Cross and Beaconsfield (each 4½ miles). Now (1949) there are also Seer Green (1 mile) and Uxbridge (12 miles). From Gerrards Cross and Uxbridge there are omnibuses which carry passengers to Gold Hill, which is nearly 2 miles from Welders House. From Seer Green a passenger must walk or hire a conveyance. Before the days when at least one visit a week to a cinema or other place of amusement is demanded, and when the same number of shopping expeditions is a dire necessity, this isolation was no more than inconvenient. By 1930 it had become a serious problem. There have been projects and promises to widen and improve Welders Lane and make it fit for omnibus traffic, but up to the present they have come to nothing. When, however, this is done and a public conveyance passes within 100 yards of Welders House and along the whole northern boundary of the estate, it will make it not only potentially valuable, but extremely desirable, and it will make it possible to build there not only a large hospital for psychological cases but one for general purposes with every modern improvement.

From 1911 to 1916 Welders was used for certified convalescent patients. The reports on it were uniformly satisfactory and male as well as female patients were sent there. It was closed when St. Luke's was closed, and in 1917 it was decided to reopen it as a convalescent home for ladies suffering from mild nervous maladies. But this plan was not developed and in 1918 the house and the immediately surrounding grounds were loaned to the War Office as a Home of Rest for Army nurses suffering from strain after the First World War.

In July 1922 it was reopened for early and uncertified cases requiring treatment, and since then it was reopened at intervals for the reception of patients, but was closed in 1927.

Even during the years when Welders was lent to the War Office the Governors were considering plans for making use of the place. Plans of several of the most modern mental hospitals were examined and a firm of surveyors was asked to take the levels of the ground there. Not only did they take the levels, but they produced sketches and a scheme for the general lay-out of a hospital. As, however, they had no experience in the construction and design of such an institution, the Committee decided to send their sketches to an architect of experience, and Mr. H. Oldred Scott was invited to submit a design "for a villa". Apparently the idea that the Committee had in mind was a hospital consisting of several villas, so as to facilitate the classification and sub-division of patients. Possibly at this time they had not formed any very definite idea of what they wanted and there is some evidence of division of opinion both on procedure and objective. But the eventual decision, made at the beginning of 1920, was that it was desirable to establish a clinic in London, mainly for out-patients but with a few beds for in-patients and to reopen Welders House.

In due course Mr. Scott submitted plans of a proposed villa and a general plan of the hospital buildings which he suggested. These were carefully considered and a majority of the Committee decided that it was unnecessary to call for competing designs, but to appoint Mr. Scott architect of the hospital. The plans were sent back to him and he was asked to embody some amendments.

The discussion of these plans and the search for a house

that could be converted without difficulty into a clinic both continued throughout 1921 without finality in the case of the former or success in that of the latter.

Meanwhile, as has been related elsewhere, in 1922 and 1923 the minds of the Committee and Dr. Gilmour were fully occupied with the small clinic in the Middlesex Hospital, and it was not until 1924 that Welders and Mr. Scott's plans seem even to have been discussed after having been in abeyance for about three years.

The Committee were now doubtful whether it would be wise to build there at all, in view of the medical opinion that the Institution would be in a position to do better work if it were situated nearer London. So once again Welders was put into cold storage. But the Committee do not seem ever to have been able to relinquish the idea of making use of the property. In 1926 they decided that it ought to be reopened for some fourteen suitable cases with a Matron and three or four nurses and four domestic servants. Next year it was inspected by a Commissioner after which the Board of Control wrote that they were prepared to issue a provisional certificate for patients. The Committee applied for this and instructed the Secretary to engage the necessary staff.

During this year the perennial plans for widening Welders Lane were again put forward by the local authorities. Up to date (1949) however, nothing has been done, and the transport problem still exists.

It was reported that the place had cost £1,279 in 1930 and Messrs. Farebrother Ellis were asked to report:

(1) Whether it would be possible to obtain a fair price for Welders House and a minimum area of the surrounding land.
(2) Whether it would be possible to let the house with the immediately surrounding ground, including the garden.
(3) Whether the remainder of the land not sold or let should be retained.
(4) Would the estate be relatively more valuable with or without the house.

In the meantime the Committee decided to keep the house closed, to cease all farming, to let the meadows for grazing, to reduce the gardening staff and to cut down expenses as far as possible.

After this no further action was taken beyond settling Mr. Oldred Scott's claim for the work he had done, and the house remained closed until 1939.

That year an offer was made by a married couple who stated that they were interested in the work of St. Luke's Hospital, to rent Welders as a private nursing and convalescent home. Their offer included the necessary repairs to the house, its connection with the Company's water, re-wiring, etc., all free of cost to St. Luke's, on condition that they became tenants at a peppercorn rent for a period of years.

This offer was accepted in principle by the Committee who authorised the Secretary to settle the details of the lease. After further negotiations it became clear that the original altruistic and somewhat optimistic terms offered were being modified and had become very definitely commercial.

Eventually a lease was granted from the 25th March, 1940, of the house and garden for seven years at a rent of £350 a year. The hospital was to have the right to determine the lease at any time after the conclusion of hostilities or the 25th March, 1943. The lessees were to expend at once £1,300 on the house, this sum to be repaid to them out of rent.

After two years the tenants found that they were unable to make Welders pay on these terms, and asked if they might sub-let or manage Welders on behalf of St. Luke's. But the Committee decided that they would prefer to accept a surrender of this lease and that any new one would be granted direct to new tenants without any intermediary. If this offer were accepted they would repay to the out-going tenants the capital they had expended on the house less the rent due.

On this basis the old lease was terminated and a new one granted in July 1942 to the Sisters of the Bon Secours, as a branch of St. Joseph's Nursing Home, Beaconsfield, until March 1947.

The grazing and shooting rights continued to be let as was also Welders Orchard, the small house at the eastern extremity of the property.

When Welders was vacated in April 1947 the Governors decided, on the advice of their medical staff, to reopen the house as a country branch for mild neuroses and convalescents.

They realised that this would be expensive, for although the house was partly furnished and they had been able to buy some of the out-going tenant's effects, it would be necessary to spend a large sum on equipment. Moreover, at this time there was a risk that the house, if left empty, might be re-quisitioned.

In October 1948 after the house had been opened for just over a year the House Committee recommended that it should be closed because:

(1) The proportion of the house that can be occupied by patients is small for there is no separate accommodation for nursing and domestic staff.

(2) The place is isolated and difficult of access.

(3) It had proved difficult to obtain and keep staff.

(4) It is too small to justify the employment of an experienced physician and existing circumstances made it almost impossible to get young house physicians.

It was recommended that the house should be put on a care and maintenance basis but that the garden should be kept up.

This recommendation was approved by the Board of the Middlesex Hospital.

XI

THE INTERREGNUM BETWEEN THE CLOSING OF THE OLD STREET HOSPITAL AND THE FOUNDATION OF WOODSIDE, A HOSPITAL FOR NERVOUS AND FUNCTIONAL DISORDERS

1917-1930

WHEN the hospital was closed finally early in 1917, the Governors owned two properties, namely Nether Court, in Kent (sold in 1921) and Welders, in Buckinghamshire, with more than 100 acres. They had also a lease of 19 Nottingham Place, W., which was the headquarters of their Private Nursing Department, initiated some nine years previously, and likewise used as the office of the Charity. Subsequently they acquired the lease of a house in Clarendon Road, Leeds, as a Headquarters of a provincial branch of the Private Nursing Department. They had also, of course, a considerable general fund invested in Trustee Securities, to which had been added about £76,000 which was available from their share of the purchase price of the hospital after the loan from the bankers for buying the Welders Estate had been repaid.

In 1917 there was no possibility of building a third St. Luke's Hospital at Welders or anywhere else. The war continued for another twenty-one months after the closing of the old hospital and subsequently shortage of materials and labour with some industrial unrest made it necessary to defer any thought of building operations. But circumstances had for some years been stimulating medical thought and science and it was evident that the future form of the Charity should be somewhat different from what it had been during the last 166 years.

When the Committee met in March 1919, they decided that they wanted more information as to the possibility of opening a clinic in London where non-certifiable cases could receive advice and treatment.

To the great sorrow of the Governors, Dr. William Rawes, F.R.C.S., had died quite unexpectedly soon after the closing of the hospital. He was a man of great ability and had been associated with St. Luke's for 26 years, for the last 19 of which he had been Medical Superintendent. His loss, at the zenith of his life, was keenly felt by all who knew him, and by none more than by the members of the Committee, who would have been so glad of his experience, wisdom and professional ability when they were starting and organising the new hospital.

They were fortunate however, in being able to call to their counsels Dr. R. W. Gilmour who, as Assistant Medical Superintendent at St. Luke's had worked for many years with Dr. Rawes. He was already in touch with the Treasurer and had suggested that part at least of the new hospital should be on the lines of a general hospital, that is to say acceptance of patients without certification and at their own wish. He made a preliminary report to the Committee about starting an out-patient clinic, and, as a temporary measure, was asked to attend at Nottingham Place to give advice and treatment to out-patients.

At the same time it was felt that, though any serious building was not possible, plans might be made and considered for a new institution. The Committee's idea was a main hospital consisting of a series of "villas" at Welders with a clinic in London. Consideration of these plans and search for a house in London that could be converted into a clinic continued without finality or success until early in 1922 when an entirely new proposal led to abandoning the idea of an independent clinic in London. Dr. Gilmour, who had been in constant communication and consultation with Dr. C. Hubert Bond, a Commissioner of the Board of Control, submitted a report, in which he stated that Dr. Bond's advice was that a psychiatric clinic should be instituted by St. Luke's, in co-operation with a General Hospital in some manner to be determined by mutual agreement. Subsequently Dr. Bond attended a Committee meeting called to discuss this proposal and supported it strongly. His opinion was:

(a) That it was essential for every mental hospital to make adequate provision for the early treatment of psycho-neurotic cases as out-patients.

(b) That by far the best way to do this was by the association of a mental with a general hospital where a

143

psychiatric clinic existed; such an arrangement not only enabled the work to be carried out with the maximum efficiency, but the public would be likely to go to the clinic of a general hospital far more willingly and with greater confidence than to one known to be part of a mental hospital. Such an association, Dr. Bond told the Committee, had been established in Oxford between the Radcliff Infirmary and the County Mental Hospital and had been working for some time with great success.

The proposal was accepted in principle and the Treasurer was authorised to approach the authorities of the Middlesex Hospital on the lines suggested by Dr. Bond.

Five months later, in October 1922, the Treasurer told the Committee of the steps he had taken and of the progress made. He first reminded them that the desirability of establishing an out-patient and in-patient clinic had been discussed and considered for the past three years. The difficulties in connection with such a project were well known to them and it was not until Dr. Bond had given them his views, that the way seemed open for an attempt to co-operate with a general hospital. He was now able to tell them that his informal proposal to the authorities of the Middlesex Hospital had been warmly welcomed, and to put before them the general outline of a scheme, already approved in principle by the Board of the Middlesex, as the basis of a formal agreement between the two hospitals. It was as follows:

(1) The objective was to co-operate with the Middlesex Hospital in the medical and nursing work of their neurological clinic.

(2) To this end St. Luke's would make a loan of £2,000 to the Middlesex, in order to cover constructional expenses which the scheme involved.

(3) St. Luke's would defray the maintenance charge of six beds according to the rate prevailing each year as declared in the audited accounts.

(4) St. Luke's would provide trained and certificated nurses as required for duty in two wards of three beds each, and would pay their salaries and incidental expenses.

(5) St. Luke's would defray the professional services of a physician attending this branch of the clinic.

In the schedule to this deed the obligations of the two hospitals were defined.

It had been pointed out that to allot two fully equipped wards and to provide a room for the physician, the Governors of the Middlesex would have to incur expenses amounting to about £2,000. It had, therefore, been suggested that St. Luke's should advance this sum as a loan, to be repaid if either hospital terminated the agreement. In the schedule, details regarding the rate of interest, credits in favour of St. Luke's, contributions by patients and the keeping of accounts, were laid down.

The Committee approved the draft agreement with the exception of a few minor points on which further information was required, and authorised the Treasurer to settle the question with the Middlesex and then to have a Deed of Agreement drawn up by the solicitors to be submitted for confirmation by both governing bodies. They appointed Dr. R. Withers Gilmour to be the Physician of the Clinic.

In March 1923 the Deed of Agreement, as approved by the Committee, was confirmed and sealed by the General Court of St. Luke's.

At the end of the year, Dr. Gilmour gave the following account of the work of the Middlesex and St. Luke's Conjoint Clinic since its opening in November.

The out-patient section began work in 1922. At first he attended only once a week but before long two attendances became necessary. Cases were of the greatest variety. The majority were psychoneuroses of all types, but there were also cases of drug and alcohol habits, dementia praecox, paranoia and early acute psychoses.

Cases in the last category, though few in number, were of particular interest, as most of them were seen early enough to prevent the illness progressing to the point where certification would have been inevitable.

In the majority of cases actual curative treatment could be carried out, and even in cases where, from the nature of the complaint, such treatment was out of the question, practical help could be given by advice and instruction.

In many cases of psychoneurosis the symptoms were of old standing and fixed, the patients having attended other institutions without benefit. These old-standing cases, however, appeared less frequently as time went on. It was reported that they were tedious to deal with, occupied much time and could rarely be benefited.

In more recent cases, results had been surprisingly good. The main line of treatment consisted in some form of psycho-therapy. For this purpose a careful physical examination was made first, to exclude or secure adequate treatment for any physical disease. Then a very accurate history was obtained of the symptoms from their commencement. Whilst getting this, a sympathetic interest had to be shown, if the confidence of the patient, so essential for treatment, was to be won. It would be easily understood that to do this with patients who were always voluble and quite unused to anyone who would listen to them, was a long and wearisome matter, but requiring close attention.

On the 12th June, 1923, the Ward Block had been officially opened. It consisted of two three-bedded wards, a small treatment room, and a ward kitchen. This small treatment room had been of great value both for in- and out-patients.

The block was of medical importance, marking as it did the first definite step in modern times towards treating functional nervous and mental diseases, as in-patients in the wards of a general hospital.

Between June and the end of the year a total of seventeen patients had been admitted; of these two men and two women were still in hospital at the end of the year.

Of the male admissions one was suffering from early manic-depressive psychosis. He was a case who would undoubtedly have been certified if he had not been admitted to this ward. He had had an outbreak of violence on the day before admission, but afterwards agreed to come into hospital. His condition on admission was such as to cause grave doubts as to the possibility of keeping him. Within a few days, however, he began to settle down, and in two months he was sent out convalescent. He went for a holiday and on his return came to see Dr. Gilmour who found him perfectly recovered. In this case the St. Luke's Ward was able to accomplish something which, under the then Lunacy Laws, a mental hospital could not have done. It was certain that any attempt to get this man to go to a mental hospital, involving his signing a form of admission, would have led to renewed resistance and probably violence on his part, and so have compelled certification; his main dread being of having to go to an asylum. When he arrived at the ward it was pointed out to him that he was coming into a general hospital, that he could not be admitted unless he wished to come in, and that he could leave whenever he liked. On this he agreed to remain with the result recorded.

In 1924 the Committee again considered building at Welders. As mentioned elsewhere plans had already been made and practically approved for a modern registered hospital, but the project had remained in abeyance while the clinic in the Middlesex Hospital was being developed.

Hitherto the general idea had been to re-start St. Luke's with the following three branches:

(*a*) An out-patients branch and a small clinic for in-patients at the Middlesex.
(*b*) A reception hospital in London.
(*c*) A hospital for certified and chronic cases at Welders.

But now it seemed doubtful whether it would be wise to establish such a hospital at Welders, because:

(1) The transport difficulty had not been overcome and it would be inconvenient for consultants to go there and expensive for the friends of poor patients to visit them.
(2) The estate was dependent for its water supply on its own well. This was reasonably satisfactory, but could not be depended on if there was any extension and it would be essential to connect the house with Company's water.
(3) Medical opinion was that more progressive and advanced work could be done at a hospital that was in or near London and not in an isolated position such as Welders.

At the end of 1924 Mr. Arthur Crofts Powell decided that he would not seek re-election as Treasurer. He was now over 80 and had been Treasurer for 23 and a Governor for 38 years. The Court and Committee accepted his resignation with great regret and warm thanks for the work he had done for St. Luke's. He was the fourth member of his family to hold this office and the policy of St. Luke's Hospital had been guided and its finances guarded by a Powell during 76 of the 174 years of its existence.

At a subsequent meeting the Rt. Hon. Lord Blanesburgh

was elected Treasurer. He presided over the Committee for the first time in October 1925 when with characteristic clarity he reviewed salient points in the past history of the Charity. While appreciating the difficulties of the Committee in deciding their future course of action he said that he hoped they would now agree that the time was opportune to proceed with the important trust that had been committed to their care. This task would require serious consideration and he suggested that, while they were rightly awaiting the results and the recommendations of the Royal Commission on Lunacy Reform, it would be wise to obtain the considered opinions of experts on the various points involved so as to make the third St. Luke's Hospital as efficient as possible, and worthy of the Charity's past reputation.

The Committee agreed that Mr. (now Lord) Macmillan, Chairman of the Royal Commission should be consulted by Mr. E. Charles, K.C., a member of the Committee, while Drs. Whitwell and Gilmour should consult Dr. Bond of the Board of Control and invite him to advise the Committee as he had already done in the matter of the Middlesex Clinic.

A small Sub-Committee was also appointed to report on and inspect possible sites, and it was suggested that a member of the Middlesex Hospital Board should be an *ex-officio* member of the Committee.

At the next meeting, Dr. Bond gave his views about the work of a modern mental hospital for curative treatment, and discussed with the Committee the various considerations connected with such a hospital, namely the area required, the type of buildings that were most convenient, the nursing staff and so forth.

Dr. Gilmour also made a report based on his investigations. He recommended a site of not less than 5 acres, convenient to a tube station or bus route. He was definitely against building on the Welders estate for the reasons given above.

From the first the new Treasurer was anxious that the hospital should be of such a kind that it would not come under the Board of Control. But before buying an estate and building the hospital there were problems which had to be solved. These were, first, to make certain whether St. Luke's could legally spend their funds on such a project and second to ascertain whether the Charity Commissioners would raise

148

any objection to such expenditure from their point of view.

Both points were satisfactorily settled thanks largely to the help and advice of Mr. Macmillan, who had now joined the Committee, as was also the possible difficulty of transferring patients to the new hospital from Welders, which was registered and might also have to be used.

Throughout 1926 various sites were inspected by the indefatigable Sub-Committee, and such were the difficulties of finding what was wanted as regards size, situation and soil, that the Committee even turned again to the idea of building. At length, however, they reported favourably on a site near Muswell Hill, namely Norton Lees, a large villa standing in its own grounds. It was for sale as the lease was about to expire, and Roseneath, another house of the same type next door, was also in the market. In both cases the freehold belonged to the Ecclesiastical Commissioners. It was also found that the tenant of a third house, Lea Wood, would sell if he might remain in the house on a full repairing lease for seven years determinable by the lessee at the end of the seventh, or by his executor in the event of his death, at 5 per cent. on the purchase price.

The Ecclesiastical Commissioners agreed, if St. Luke's acquired the leasehold interest in these three properties for use as a hospital, to sell their reversionary interests in them.

The three houses were next to one another, and were the only residences in Woodside Avenue. Together they had a frontage of 220 yards on this road, with attractive gardens and good trees in an area totalling altogether about 6 acres.

Both the agents and the architect Mr. T. A. Pole, F.R.I.B.A., reported well on them. By the end of the year Messrs. Farebrother Ellis & Son stated that the freehold and leasehold of the three could be obtained for the following sums:

Norton Lees	£5,000
Roseneath	£5,500
Plot opposite Roseneath	£ 200
Lea Wood	£7,500
Ecclesiastical Commrs.	£3,500 for their freehold interest.

On this the Committee instructed their solicitors to receive and consider provisional contracts from the owners.

In January Mr. Pole submitted provisional plans for a hospital of 100 beds with administrative offices for 55, but the Committee decided to start with 50 beds.

It was proposed to link up the existing houses by corridors or covered ways to the wards and a treatment block to the north of them, to enlarge Norton Lees as a nurses' home and to build an administrative block between that house and Roseneath. In the original plans there were also a Recreation Room and an Operating Theatre. It was explained to the Ecclesiastical Commissioners that the idea was to create one hospital unit of the three houses, and this idea was accepted by them as coming within the terms of the contract for the sale of their freehold interest.

The Board of Control were taking a keen and most friendly interest in the new hospital and the plans were submitted to them in order to take advantage of their great experience. Indeed throughout the building operations Dr. Bond was always ready to lend his knowledge to the Committee.

By July the revised plans were accepted by all concerned, and the architect was asked to produce working drawings and to get tenders for the building by the end of the year. These, however, were not laid before the Committee until March of the following year. They ranged from £94,494 to £106,600. The cost was a shock to the Governors and they decided that it must be cut down.

At this point it should be noted that Mr. A. B. Nutter, O.B.E., who had joined the Committee in 1926, was appointed Under-Treasurer and authorised to settle details. From this time onwards he was intimately concerned with every aspect of the new hospital, and subsequently with its administration.

On a further review of the plans and the tender of Messrs. Walter Lawrence & Son it was decided that the cost could be reduced by leaving out the Recreation Block and Operating Theatre, thus saving £12,162.

Even so, at least one governor expressed doubts about the wisdom of spending so much of their capital. The Committee, however, in the words of the minutes, "considered at length the question of building the clinic and reviewed its working relation as part of the scheme for re-establishing St. Luke's as a modern mental hospital . . . and resolved to proceed with the scheme as modified and to accept Messrs. Walter Lawrence's tender as reduced." The Court also approved the "building a part of the new St. Luke's Hospital at Muswell Hill."

It is clear, therefore, that at this stage the hospital at Muswell Hill was to be the unregistered part of the new St. Luke's Hospital, free from any association with certified mental incapacity and therefore from official inspection and control of any sort. This position was fully accepted by the Board of Control. Nevertheless when the General Court finally approved the contract with the builders, they noted that the plans "had been approved by the Board of Control".

Actual building began on the 21st May, 1928, and the Woodside Hospital was completed, furnished and equipped ready for the formal opening ceremony soon after the middle of 1930.

XII

WOODSIDE HOSPITAL FROM 1930 TO 1948. THE PART OF THE HOSPITAL IN THE WAR 1939-1945

1930-1948

THE closing of St. Luke's Hospital in 1916 marked the end of an epoch in the history of the Charity. In 1750 it had been created as "A Hospital for Poor Lunatics". At that period lunacy was regarded as a temporary and curable disease, but from 1862 onwards the distinction between this and other forms of insanity gradually ceased to exist, with the result that as time went on St. Luke's practically became a mental hospital in the modern sense of the word. When the Old Street site was sold, and St. Luke's, as a hospital, ceased temporarily to exist, the thoughts of the governing body and their medical advisors turned towards those sufferers whose nerves were sick, but who were not, as a rule, treated in a general hospital. On the other hand if they were sent to a mental hospital and had to associate with the patients there, their surroundings might well increase the mental strain in such cases and possibly aggravate their illness.

The outcome of such thoughts was the experiment made in collaboration with the Middlesex Hospital. This was at first viewed doubtfully in some quarters, but its success, already described, was incontestable, and the decision to build a hospital for such cases was taken very largely as a result of what had been done at the Middlesex Clinic.

The aim of the hospital cannot be better described than in the words of the Treasurer, Lord Blanesburgh, who, shortly before the opening, wrote to *The Times* as follows:

"Her Highness the Princess Helena Victoria has graciously consented formally to open Woodside Nerve Hospital. . . It will, I feel sure, be of interest to many to know something of an event which may be claimed to be unique in the history of the treatment of nervous disorders in England.

"The new building is the outcome of an endeavour on the part of the Governors of St. Luke's Hospital to establish out of the available resources of their foundation, a modern institution, free from official control and under disinterested management, for the treatment by the latest and most scientific methods of the many functional and nervous disorders, to which, in an ever-increasing degree, all classes, and most especially the educated classes, appear in these days of stress, to be subject. The need of an institution exclusively devoted to the enlightened care and treatment of such cases has, for some years, been recognised by the medical profession. It is hoped that by this new hospital the need has, to some small extent, been met.

"The buildings stand in grounds of some $6\frac{3}{4}$ acres . . . near Highgate Woods, surrounded by gardens.

"The Hospital is believed to possess all requirements of modern practice. It has been constructed, arranged and furnished, so as to minister to the comfort and well-being of the patients, for whom the latest discoveries in scientific treatment will be available.

"The capital expenditure of purchase, building and equipment has been borne by St. Luke's. The amount has been large, but the Governors look to no pecuniary return.

"The remaining resources of their charity are, however, unequal to the further heavy cost of running the hospital, and current expenses must, to some substantial extent, be met by payments from the patients themselves. Only, however, to a substantial extent.

"The need for such a hospital is most urgent in the cases of educated people of slender means, who, while shrinking from entry into a public institution, cannot afford the necessarily high charges for private individual treatment. It is hoped that to none of these sufferers need any charge be made in excess of a sum which bears some relation to current cost, while every effort will be made to see that no charge in any deserving case is prohibitive. It is even hoped that from larger payments made by patients who can afford to make them, supplemented by some further assistance from St. Luke's, this ancient Charity may be enabled, in meritorious cases . . . to maintain to the full its benevolent aims and purposes."

On the 31st December, 1930, about seven weeks after the opening there were 12 patients; during 1931 there were 26 in the hospital.

Here it is necessary to describe briefly the somewhat complicated status and organisation of St. Luke's Hospital in 1930. In the first place, St. Luke's, though a hospital in name, was not one in fact. It was a charity owning properties and supporting some institutions. The properties consisted of the general fund, the Welders estate in Buckinghamshire, and the Woodside property at Muswell Hill. The institutions were Woodside Hospital, the six beds in the Middlesex Hospital and the private nursing establishments in London and Leeds. These latter were closed soon after the opening of Woodside. The house at Welders was registered by the Board of Control.

Since the death of the Duke of Leeds in 1927, St. Luke's had been without a President. In 1931 Major-General the Rt. Hon. the Earl of Athlone, who had always been interested in the work of hospitals, consented to have his name put forward for this office, and was elected President of St. Luke's and Woodside. In June of that year at a special meeting of the Committee he was welcomed to the hospital where he inspected every department and detail with keen interest. He has been re-elected every year until the National Health Act came into force and the office lapsed.

It was about this time that three ladies were elected Governors and appointed to the Committee. Thus, at last was reversed the Committee's refusal in 1825 to allow ladies to have any part in the government of the hospital. These ladies added their full share to the general knowledge of a governing body whose wisdom and administrative experience were of high value to Woodside Hospital, particularly during its early and experimental stages.

The story of the hospital was not, however, uneventful during these years. It was one of steady unadvertised progress. Indeed, at one time it was felt that the work that was being done there was not as well known among the medical profession as it should be, and steps were taken to extend the knowledge of its activities.

After 1927, Welders remained closed. The Governors considered that, while the new hospital was being developed, it would be wise to limit their other activities. Therefore, apart from some cultivation and the supply of some fruit and vegetables to Woodside, little was done with this potentially valuable asset. Expenses were reduced as far as possible by letting the shooting and grazing rights, and the small house, Welders Orchard, which had been occupied by the Secretary, Mr. W. H. Baird, until he retired in 1932.

He had been in the service of St. Luke's for nearly 42 years, having been appointed Steward in August 1890, and Secretary-Steward in 1896. The Governors showed their appreciation of his long and valuable service by granting him a pension, appointing him a life Governor, and electing him to the Committee.

Mr. Alfred Nutter, O.B.E., who, as Under-Treasurer since 1927 had a detailed knowledge of Woodside (and who indeed had been one of the guiding spirits of the new hospital from the time when its site had been chosen) was appointed Secretary.

Woodside proved to be a costly institution. This was inevitable in a small hospital where overhead charges are bound to be heavy in proportion to the total cost. In any case a hospital for nervous diseases is more expensive than one for general illness, because the medical and nursing staff have to give much time to individual patients and therefore their numbers are high in proportion to the number of beds. Not only were such expenses relatively high, but the price of everything continued to rise yearly.

It is interesting to compare the expenditure of the old St. Luke's with Woodside. Between the years 1875 and 1915 the annual expenditure on the old hospital averaged £12,390, with a tendency during these 40 years to rise gradually but not excessively. The average number of patients in the hospital was 182.

The average annual expenditure on Woodside during the five years, 1935 to 1940 was £16,030, and the number of patients at one time was about 44.

These comparisons are not (and do not pretend to be) exact. The standard of the smaller hospital was much higher in every respect than the old one, and was probably higher than in most small hospitals of the same period dealing with general illness. But they are given in order to show that the Governors of St. Luke's had now a much more difficult financial situation to deal with than their predecessors and that their decision not to open Welders for patients was prudent.

Despite the high standard and the fact that there were no fees for medical attendance and no extras of any kind, the average weekly cost of a patient during the years 1932-1937 was £7 3s. 6d., which seems to show that the administration was as economical as it was efficient.

In the early medical reports the importance of psycho-therapy was stressed and it was agreed that it must be regarded as an integral and essential part of the treatment at Woodside. The first visiting psychotherapist was appointed in October 1933.

The medical staff also urged that occupational therapy should be placed on a more regular footing. At first it was found, contrary to experience in the old hospital, that it was easier to induce the men to take up some handicraft than to interest the women in any artistic work other than knitting or sewing, but, when a trained Occupational Therapy Officer was appointed in 1934, this form of treatment received considerable stimulus.

Dr. R. Withers Gilmour retired in July 1935 after a con-nection with St. Luke's Hospital since June 1895 when he joined the staff as a Clinical Assistant. He held this post for a year before he moved on to gain further experience. In September 1901 he returned as Assistant Medical Officer under Dr. William Rawes and remained on the staff until October 1914 when he resigned in order to take up private practice. But in 1919 he was again employed by St. Luke's and, as has been related, he was largely instrumental in starting and taking charge of the clinic at the Middlesex Hospital. During the building of Woodside he was closely concerned with the design and arrangement of the hospital of which he became the first Physician-in-Charge.

In addition to granting him a pension on his retirement as a reward for his long and valued service, the Governors gave him a personal presentation as a testimony of their warm regard, for he had won to a special degree the affection and esteem, not only of patients and staff, but of all who knew him.

He was succeeded by Dr. Noel Harris, who had been Chief Assistant to the Department of Psychological Medicine at St. Thomas's Hospital and Assistant Medical Officer at

Springfield Mental Hospital. Almost simultaneously with his appointment to Woodside, he was appointed Physician for Psychological Medicine to the Middlesex Hospital and lecturer on Psychological Medicine to the Middlesex Hospital Medical School. He has held these appointments ever since, and of his services to Woodside more will be related hereafter.

This is not a history of the medical treatment at Woodside, of which the author is wholly unqualified to write, but some extracts from the annual medical reports are pertinent in that they will tell the experiments and progress made since the hospital was first opened.

In 1937 Dr. Harris wrote:

"It has again been obvious that a very high percentage of the people seeking admission are suffering from primary or reactive Depression, and the number of persons suffering from a pure Neurosis is relatively small. This is an important point to remember in considering future development.

"The Anxiety Neuroses, particularly those who have a good previous personality history, do well. Those who have always been the anxiety type, with a history of having worried over trifles all their lives, must be regarded as unlikely to respond so quickly or so satisfactorily.

"Theoretically, the Hysterics should do well, and those cases of recent onset who have a good personality respond excellently. Unfortunately, often only the worst and most chronic Hysteric is sent to the Hospital. An elderly Hysteric who has had symptoms of chronic physical illness for many years is one of the hardest of all patients to cure, especially if lacking in volition.

"It is important to remember, in considering the suitability of patients for Psychotherapy, that they should be intelligent, possess some driving force, and not be too old.

"The Obsessional patients can usually be helped considerably, but absolute cure is rare and needs a prolonged stay in Hospital.

"The primary depressions, particularly if they are of the reactive type, can generally be helped a great deal. But their stay in Hospital is likely to be a matter of three to six months, and if they or their friends have been told that a few weeks in Hospital will be sufficient, it puts the staff in a false position.

157

"Those Schizophrenics who are not very introverted, whose phantasy life is not too rich and who have an acute episode, can often be helped greatly. Many make a satisfactory adjustment for a time, but give the impression that they will not face the realities of life by themselves for very long.

"Those cases of Alcoholism which are admitted do well, but it is essential that they should have some cause for their Alcoholism, and that the physical condition is not permanently impaired by what they have already consumed.

"After much consideration it was considered inadvisable to make use of the new Insulin Shock Therapy for Schizophrenia, but in the spring of 1937 we were introduced to the even later Cardiazol Shock Therapy . . . and in May gave what is believed to the first injection given in England. Some interesting and encouraging results were obtained, and Dr. Hobson gave a brief account of his work with Cardiazol at a meeting of the Psychiatric Section of the Royal Society of Medicine.

"Briefly, the treatment consists of giving the patient an intravenous injection of Cardiazol as rapidly as possible. . . . If the injection is successful the result is to produce in the patient a convulsive reaction resembling an epileptic fit. It is perhaps one of the most dramatic forms of treatment in existence. The patient rapidly comes round, has a considerable amount of amnesia for the event, and within an hour or two is usually able to get up and dress. In some cases benefit has been noticed after one to five injections.

"The treatment is being continued and is now being combined with Insulin which is the latest technique advocated.

"Treatment by Prolonged Narcosis has been continued with real success. Dr. H. A. Palmer was awarded the degree of M.D. (Manchester) by virtue of a Thesis on the value of continuous Narcosis in the Treatment of Mental Disorders. The patients most likely to benefit from this treatment are those suffering from an agitated or depressive state. Sometimes the treatment of severe Anxiety Neurosis can be initiated with prolonged Narcosis, psychotherapy being more easily undertaken after it.

"Two patients illustrate the effects of narcosis. A man aged 35 had what was diagnosed as an acute attack of influenza at a time when he was seriously overworked. He got over this and then developed an attack of acute Confusion and Depression, which, if it had developed, would almost certainly have needed treatment in a mental hospital. He was given a course of Prolonged Narcosis lasting a fortnight, obtained from 16 to 22 hours sleep out of the 24, and within a month was discharged perfectly well.

"A young married woman, aged 21, whose upbringing had not been a happy one, and who had recently been through much mental stress, became elated, excited and grossly extravagant. She was getting rapidly worse when she was admitted and given a course of Prolonged Narcosis. Within a fortnight of the end of the course she was practically normal and continued to make an uninterrupted recovery."

The progress of the hospital continued steadily. The average daily number of patients shows its numerical growth:

$$\begin{array}{ccc}
\text{In } 1935 \text{ it was} & 34.78 \\
\text{,, } 1936 \text{ ,,} & \text{,, } & 44.24 \\
\text{,, } 1937 \text{ ,,} & \text{,, } & 45.12 \\
\text{,, } 1938 \text{ ,,} & \text{,, } & 47.57
\end{array}$$

In 1937 the Committee decided that the time had come to give notice to the Middlesex that they must determine the agreement with that hospital, as it was felt that the maintenance of the six beds in the Neurological Clinic was now a burden rather than a benefit and that the experiment had given both hospitals the experience they required. Formal notice was accordingly given early in 1938 and the Middlesex repaid the loan of £2,000 which St. Luke's had contributed to meet the extra expenses involved when the Clinic had been initiated.

Miss L. A. Hunt, who had then been in the service of St. Luke's since 1912 (when she was appointed Matron at Welders), resigned her appointment and was succeeded by Miss I. E. Tebbutt in May 1937.

During 1938, number 28 Grand Avenue was taken into use as a home for the night nurses. Lea Wood became vacant the same year and, although the house was not used, the patients had the benefit of the additional garden and ground.

The possible expansion of the hospital by the use of Lea

Wood stimulated consideration of future development. A paper by Dr. Harris, outlining the possible development of Woodside as a complete unit for psychological medicine, and plans and sketches by Mr. O. P. Milne, F.R.I.B.A., the hospital's architect, were discussed by the Committee, and after various suggestions had been made it was decided in June 1939 that Lea Wood should be altered so as to be available as an additional ward at a cost of not more than £3,000. Hardly had this decision been reached when a telegram giving warning of war was received from the Ministry of Health.

Already, in the autumn of 1938, there had been the so-called Munich Crisis. On that occasion, so vague and uncertain were the indications of the role of the hospital in case of war, that no modifications of existing arrangements could be made. Some preliminary steps to ensure the safety of patients and staff were, however, taken. Trenches were dug; gas-proof chambers were provided, and various emergency stores were bought.

Following the "Stand by" telegram of the 25th August, further admissions were restricted and preparations were made for the evacuation of all those who could be sent home. Actual evacuation followed the receipt of a subsequent telegram and was completed in three days.

Meanwhile, of course, all work on Lea Wood was stopped.

During the next month the hospital was in a state of suspended animation with a full staff and no patients. The opportunity was taken to give a series of lectures to the nursing staff. In October, Dr. Harris reported to the Committee that the hospital had been considered for various Emergency Services, but finally he had been told that it would be open for neuroses and mild psychoses among officers, male and female, of His Majesty's Forces, and some of the Civilian Defence Forces. This decision was given to him verbally and was not put into writing then or subsequently. Dr. Harris, himself, was to be in charge, provided he could find time to teach psychiatry to Middlesex Hospital students. He was also to be available for consultation in various hospitals in the north-west sector of London.

Owing to the ease with which the hospital had been evacuated, permission was given to admit some private patients at 7½ or 5½ guineas per week.

So far the financial responsibility of the Ministry for Service

(E.M.S.) patients had not been made clear, and the Committee, therefore, were glad of this permission to admit some private patients at their discretion.

A war Sub-Committee was appointed soon after the outbreak of war to be available at short notice, and this "War Emergency Committee", as it came to be known, remained in being until 1945 and dealt with most problems as they arose, regardless of whether they were strictly the concern of the General or the House Committee.

The early weeks of 1940 were very difficult. Drs. Palmer and Hubert joined the R.A.M.C. and Dr. Hobson left for the R.N.V.R. For a week Dr. Harris was single-handed, until Dr. Laetitia Millard joined in January. There were then 23 private patients in the hospital. In April the numbers had risen to 42, of whom 12 were E.M.S.

Later in the year, Drs. Nathan, T. A. Ross, late of Cassell's Hospital, and R. Moody, joined the staff.

Meanwhile, no payments had been received from the Ministry for the E.M.S. patients, and the Physician-in-Charge and the Secretary, already burdened by shortage of staff and additional duties (like almost everyone else) had their difficulties increased by the ill-defined official position of the hospital. To all other hospitals had been sent a special and elaborate financial form, showing how to claim payment for E.M.S. patients, but Woodside did not receive one until the Secretary, after some delay, had secured a copy. Possibly the somewhat complicated organisation of St. Luke's Hospital may have contributed to "thick mists which had enshrouded the hospital from the eyes of the Ministry of Health" at this period. During much of this time, the Physician-in-Charge, the Secretary and the Assistant Secretary slept in the hospital.

Gradually the position became more stable; in September, out of 49 patients, 36 were Service cases, and the staff was increased but were still much over-worked.

So far the hospital had escaped damage, but at 9.30 p.m. on the 21st October, 1940, a bomb, happily of delayed action type, fell on the lawn a few feet in front of the west end of the East Block. The patients and staff were all quickly evacuated from the wing without any confusion, and when the bomb exploded eight hours later there was no casualty of any kind. The western wall of the building was cracked from top to bottom and two-thirds of the wing were so seriously damaged as to be unusable until demolished and re-built. Dr. Harris told the Committee that every member of the staff had behaved with remarkable courage, beyond praise, and the Committee asked that their admiration and thanks should be conveyed to all of them.

For a short time there was a question whether Woodside should carry on at Muswell Hill, but it was soon agreed by everyone, including the Ministry, that the hospital should remain where it was and that Lea Wood should be taken into use with as little alteration as possible. So quickly and satisfactorily was the work in this house completed by Mr. A. Ibbetson, the hospital builder, and Mr. G. A. Sivyer, the upholsterer, that the Committee sent them their official thanks. Later, 28 Grand Avenue, previously occupied by the night staff, was opened for women patients.

The financial position was also clarified. At first an attempt was made to treat both civilian and Service patients, but the growing numbers of the latter made it impossible to continue to admit the former, and all beds had to be reserved for E.M.S. cases, and thus the hospital became almost entirely dependent on payments from the Ministry. No payment was made for beds reserved, but only for those actually occupied. This was based on the costs as calculated in the previous year's accounts. They were, therefore, provisional, and "on account", being adjusted subsequently. But they were enough to enable the hospital to continue on its usual lines without anxiety. Indeed, for the remainder of the war, income exceeded expenditure, usually by a considerable sum. This was inevitable, so long as the hospital was full of patients paid for by the Government. In normal times such a credit might have been a cause of anxiety, but during the war, when replacements, repairs and maintenance became more and more difficult, it was one rather of satisfaction. Apart from uncertainty about the future, there was no doubt that the Charity would be faced at the end of the war with very heavy bills for items such as painting and furniture.

The administrative problems also became less extemporised and more of a routine. It was not easy in a hospital where not one of the medical officers was in uniform, to treat and control patients nearly all of whom belonged to the Services and many of whom from the very nature of their illness were not always amenable. However, a Military Board to consider cases sat each week, and a Military Registrar, resident at Mill Hill, was appointed. Apart from this semi-disciplinary help it was usually found that there were one or more among the officers who, by their example and authority, set the tone amongst the rest and helped to maintain the air of serenity and content which had always characterised the hospital. The patients were, of course, nearly all of an entirely different type from those admitted before the war. For example, the presence of so many young officers made physical exercise necessary. The Army sent an Instructor Sergeant-Major of the Army Physical Training Corps to supervise games and exercises every day. The vicar of the parish allowed them to use the parish badminton hall at certain times, and the Central Foundation Schools of London gave them permission occasionally to use the large playing field next door. A few, but only a few, worked in the garden. Indoors the Committee sanctioned the use of the Board Room for dances and musical entertainments. Apart from all this, the patients were given much more freedom than they would have had in a military hospital, and on the whole, this system worked wonderfully well and smoothly.

Dr. Noel Harris divided the Service cases into groups. There were those who suffered from anxiety. After Dunkirk, the majority were exhaustion cases with some acute anxiety neuroses and hysteria. Later, chronic types of neuropaths or psychopaths predominated. They were men who could not adjust themselves to Army life, or suffered from a depressive condition similar to previous attacks in civil life. A wide range of treatments was employed. Full and modified prolonged narcosis proved very useful. Narco-analysis was used also with great success.

Some of the hardest to cure were individuals who had refused to go sick and did their utmost to "hold on" to themselves and not to give way to the shattering emotional experiences through which they had passed.

A problem that soon confronted the Medical Boards was "Attributability". At first the authorities had indicated that no Neuroses or Psychoses were to be considered attributable to war service. This seemed unfair to the hospital medical officers and they held the view that a patient's illness was attributable to the war, if he had a good previous personality history but had been through a great strain as a result of military service.

At first it was found difficult to make full use of the Occupational Therapy Department. Some officer patients were inclined to look on occupational therapy, when it took the form of artistic handicrafts, as effeminate, and such prejudices had to be overcome. By undertaking the library work, the Occupational Therapist got in touch with everyone soon after their admission, whatever their views or inhibitions might be. It was possible also to get a trained carpenter to give lessons, and these soon became popular.

The medical staff realised very quickly that in time of war a number of persons got posts of responsibility which they would not have been given in peace-time, with the result that they broke down under the strain. Others proved to be chronics who ought not to have been given commissions at all. It was felt that it was bad policy to mix such patients, many of them "left over" from the war of 1914-18, with those who had a breakdown in the present war, and whom it was hoped to cure and return to duty. The point was raised with the authorities with the result that no more chronics were sent to the hospital.

The nursing staff had a difficult time. Many patients really required very little sick nursing in the usual sense of the word. It was, therefore, a great credit to the staff that they did not give way to the occasional monotony and boredom of their work, but maintained their sympathy and good psychological approach.

A very interesting period followed D-day in 1944. At first patients were received from Normandy within a week of their becoming casualties, so acute exhaustion and anxiety states predominated. This was especially the case before the breakthrough. During that comparatively short but intense period, when our Army was confined in a small area with heavy fighting on three sides and no possibility of giving men a real rest, psychiatric casualties became heavy. For these, treatment of heavy sedation, and in some cases of narco-analysis proved effective, and the majority were returned to duty though not necessarily to the front line.

In reviewing the work of the hospital during the war, Dr. Harris wrote in his report that he thought one of its most interesting features was the great variety of sources from which patients had been drawn. Not only were officers, male and female, admitted, but patients from the Allies were taken in.

The following is a list of the services from which patients were received:

British	The Dominions
Royal Navy	Canadian Air Force
Army	New Zealand Army
R.A.F.	
Marines	*India*
Merchant Navy	Indian Army
A.T.S.	Indian Navy
W.A.A.F.	
W.R.N.S.	*Allies*
W.A.I.M.N.S.	American Army
Transport Auxiliary	Czech Army
P.M.R.A.N.S.	Polish Army
Civilian E.M.S.	French Army
U.N.R.R.A.	French Navy
Allied Control Commission	
National Fire Service	
Ex-Service	

By the close of the war with Japan 1,705 Service patients had been through the hospital. They required a great variety of treatment, and between all of them and their physicians there was always, so far as it was possible, close individual contact. Most of them had some form of psychotherapy. Prolonged narcosis was used to a large extent, and the usual medicinal treatment, including modified insulin therapy, was given particularly to those who were admitted when physically exhausted and weak. A certain number of selected cases were given fairly deep analytical treatment. During the later stages of the war, the form of psychological exploration and treatment known as "narco-analysis" was used with much success. The hospital acquired its own Electric Shock Machine in 1940, but Electric Convulsion Treatment was not given in more than a few cases, on the whole with satisfactory results.

It is not easy to put the results obtained during the war into statistic form, but some results compiled by the E.M.S. authorities showed that the percentage of officers returned to duty from Woodside was quite high. A fair percentage went back to Category A, and a large percentage to B or C. Those who were recommended for invaliding out were, as a rule, patients who were not suitable for the services at all, and either ought not to have been accepted, or placed in a very low medical category in the first instance.

No attempt is made to give statistics about improvement, for no valuable information would be obtained thereby, unless it had been possible to organise a very careful follow-up, and this, it was found, could not be done; but it can definitely be stated that all but a very few left Woodside feeling appreciably better than when they came in.

There was practically no research during these years because pressure of work made it impossible. It is hoped, however, that some case material will be published later, and that this may lead to more detailed research.

After the first few months of the war, when there were numerous changes among the medical staff, the main burden of the hospital was borne by Dr. Harris, who was Physician-in-Charge for the whole period. He was assisted by Dr. R. L. Moody and Dr. J. R. P. Edkins, both of whom were resident, and, on a Sessional basis, by Dr. E. Lincoln Williams and Dr. T. T. Bartlett.

At the end of the war, the first to return was Lt.-Col. W. H. de B. Hubert, who took up his duties on a part-time basis in June 1945, to explore and develop the possibilities of a civilian Out-Patient Department. Unfortunately, he found that the work he undertook was a very severe tax on a man whose health had suffered as a result of prolonged service abroad. This coupled with the difficulty of transport compelled him reluctantly to resign his appointment.

Lt.-Col. H. A. Palmer was the next to return. He was appointed Resident Deputy Physician-in-Charge. He took over the development of the Out-Patient Department from Dr. Hubert as well as the care and treatment of civilian in-patients and some E.M.S. patients. Prior to his return to Woodside he had applied for the post of Psychiatric Physician to the Otago University, New Zealand, with the knowledge and approval of the Committee. He was selected for it and left for New Zealand in March 1946.

Dr. J. A. Hobson also returned to the hospital as Resident

Physician and was appointed Deputy Physician-in-Charge when Dr. Palmer left.

All these physicians had given valuable and devoted service to Woodside under the leadership of Dr. Noel Harris.

Before the war the Cardiazol Treatment had been tried at Woodside before it was used anywhere else in this country. Subsequently, Electric Shock Therapy was investigated, but Dr. Palmer's visit to the U.S.A. and his enquiries there indicated that there were certain elements of danger in this form of treatment. As a result of discussions among the medical staff it was decided to substitute a treatment of Electric Shock Therapy with a combination of Curare. This was immediately before the outbreak of war, and consequently further research and investigation at Woodside was postponed until after 1945. Dr. Hobson was largely responsible for the further investigation of this form of treatment which he practically perfected in 1947.

On Drs. Noel Harris, Moody and Edkins, however, fell the prolonged wearisome and sometimes monotonous work of "carrying on" during the war years. and the debt owed to them by St. Luke's is one that cannot be repaid.

Here it is appropriate to refer to two most serious casualties which the Charity suffered during, and shortly after, the end of the war.

On the 9th February, 1943, the Secretary of St. Luke's and Woodside, Mr. Alfred Barrett Nutter, O.B.E., died after a very short illness. His loss was felt equally by the Charity and Woodside Hospital. He had been a Governor since 1926. In 1928 he was appointed Under-Treasurer, and in 1932 he succeeded Mr. Baird as Secretary.

During the building of the hospital, and ever since its opening he had given it his constant and devoted care. By his own example he set a standard that was as high as it was stimulating to everyone, and the success of the hospital during those twelve years was largely due to him. Woodside Hospital can truly be regarded as his memorial. He had gained the affection of the whole staff to whom he was both a true friend and a just chief.

Mr. Nutter was succeeded by Brigadier C. N. French, C.M.G., C.B.E., as Secretary, St. Luke's Hospital, and by Mrs. Phyllis Thompson, who had been Mr. Nutter's assistant, as Secretary, Woodside Hospital.

In August 1946 the Treasurer, Lord Blanesburgh, died. For many months his health had given grave anxiety and had not allowed him to make the journey from his home to Committee meetings. He had guided the hospital through a great part of the transition period that followed the closing of the old hospital, and it was his recognition of the possibilities of psychological medicine, coupled with his enthusiasm and energy that were largely responsible for the creation and development of Woodside Hospital. The Governors, in their resolution mourning his death, rightly stated that from 1925 to 1946 he had discharged the responsible duties of Treasurer with the highest distinction. But his chief memorial was that all, from the Governors down to the humblest employees, felt that they had lost a personal friend.

Brigadier-General Sir George Cockerill, C.B., who had been a Governor since 1930 and a Vice-President since 1937, was elected to succeed Lord Blanesburgh as Treasurer. For some years he had acted as Chairman of Committee when the Treasurer was unable to attend, and was thus fully conversant with all that concerned the hospital. At the General Court which confirmed his appointment on the 9th October, 1946, the President, Lord Athlone, presided, and subsequently inspected the hospital.

In February 1946 Dr. Henry Yellowlees was appointed Under-Treasurer. He had been a Governor for 17 years and a most valuable member and regular attendant of all Committees. The Committee felt that some special status was essential for him in view of the various negotiations that they were asking him to undertake in connection with the National Health Act, and also as some recognition of his devotion to the hospital and of the wise counsel which he had always given to the Committee.

During the war, the Governors had been faced with many and various administrative problems, of which some are worthy of mention. In 1945 the Ministry asked whether 20 or 30 additional beds could be provided at Woodside. At that time the West Wing, Lea Wood and 28 Grand Avenue (known as Dormy House) were all occupied. The Committee felt that such an enlargement, at a time when additional medical, nursing and domestic staff were all extremely difficult to obtain, was unlikely to increase efficiency, but came to the conclusion that they could not refuse the request. They replied, therefore, agreeing to the extension, but stipulating that they must have complete equipment and the provision of a reasonably full staff before any extra patients were admitted. However, the Ministry found that the required accommodation could be found elsewhere, and Woodside was saved from this sudden and extemporised expansion which might have left a whole series of problems to be solved at the end of the war.

The undamaged portion of the East Wing was for some years occupied by the Child's Guidance Training Centre on its return to London from Oxford. In 1945 Mr. Milne, F.R.I.B.A., was instructed to take the necessary preliminary steps towards rebuilding this wing. The War Damage Commission approved the tender of Messrs. Walter Lawrence & Sons (who originally built the hospital) and work was begun in June 1947. The work was completed in November 1948, and as furniture and equipment had already been bought, patients were admitted in the following December.

In 1943 the Ministry of Fuel and Power gave instructions that the hospital's heating plant must be converted from a heavy oil to a gas-burning one. This was, in fact, a concession. The original intention had been that the conversion should be from oil to solid fuel, but, apart from the difficulty of finding the extra labour that this would involve, the necessary plant was unobtainable. The conversion was completed during 1944 at a cost of £940. No compensation was received. On the whole, the system has worked very satisfactorily, but it proved expensive. There was, however, one explosion, in November 1946, due, as far as could be discovered, to an escape of gas. The second engineer was slightly injured. The Chief Engineer and the hospital heating engineers had the hot water system in working order again in three days.

During the period 1930 to 1948, the salaries of the nursing staff have been considerably increased. In 1931 they were:

For Ward Sisters	..	..	from £85 to £95 p.a.
,, Staff Nurses	..	..	,, £75 ,, £80 ,,
,, Asst. Nurses	..	..	,, £60 ,, £65 ,,

In 1938 the Committee decided to adopt a regular pension scheme for nurses and, after the examination of the various systems, settled on the Federated Superannuation Scheme for Nurses and Hospital Officers (Contributory). It came into operation on the 1st January, 1939, and was on the following basis: each month the member of the staff contributed 5 per cent. of her salary plus an arbitrary amount, representing the value of her emoluments, i.e., her board and lodging. The hospital contributed 10 per cent. The total of 15 per cent. was applied in payment of the premium on an insurance policy for a deferred annuity at the age of 55. The annual cost to the hospital at that time was about £350. The scheme was compulsory for trained, but voluntary for assistant, nurses.

Subsequently a grant was made by the Ministry of Health to voluntary hospitals in aid of increased nursing salaries, but the British Hospitals Association, which was arranging the matter on behalf of the Ministry ruled that Woodside was not a voluntary hospital within the meaning of the definition they had laid down. The Committee, which included several legal experts besides the Chairman, disagreed with this ruling. Since, however, the question was raised during the war, it was felt that in the circumstances it would be more dignified not to press their claim at that time, but to indicate why they disagreed with the Association and to make clear that they reserved their right to reopen the matter at a more convenient opportunity.

Subsequently they raised the salaries of the nursing staff as seemed right, although they had no grant to help them, with the result that, when in April 1943 they adopted in principle the salaries recommended in the Report of the Rushcliffe Committee, it was found that those given to their staff compared favourably with the recommendations of that Committee. A few adjustments were made, but by reason of their length of service many of the assistant nurses were actually receiving more than recommended by the Report.

At the end of 1944, salaries were:

For Ward Sisters	.. ..	£150 to £155 p.a.
„ Staff Nurses	.. ..	£120 p.a.
„ Asst. Nurses	.. ..	£85 to £95 p.a.

These salaries followed the adoption of further "Rushcliffe" recommendations on the salaries of nurses in mental hospitals.

Although Woodside is not a mental hospital the qualifications required of its nurses are the same as in that type of hospital. Therefore, unless identical salaries are paid, it would not be possible to get the services of the most efficient persons.

During the latter years of the war, the shortage of both nursing and domestic staff caused the governors some anxiety, and the position became rather worse after the end of the war. In June 1946 the shortage became so acute that it was necessary to limit admissions for a time. After that, however, the position improved gradually. During the really critical time the fact that the hospital was able to carry on was due largely to the admirable team spirit among both nurses and domestics.

The number of service patients became fewer with the end of the war in Europe and it was possible to admit the first post-war private patient in November 1945, but the hospital remained an E.M.S. one and service patients continued to have priority up to the "appointed day", the 5th July, 1948, when the National Health Scheme came into being, and practically all became State patients.

During the second half of 1944 the Germans started a new form of bombing, first with pilotless aeroplanes and subsequently with very large rocket projectiles. During this period bombs fell on every side of the hospital, some within a radius of less than half a mile, and it seemed that Woodside was bound, sooner or later, to be struck. Happily, however, this ordeal did not last very long, no bomb fell dangerously near to this hospital and damage was limited to a few window panes and burst doors. The Physician-in-Charge was the chief sufferer as his house at Finchley was seriously damaged by the blast of a rocket bomb which fell about 400 yards away.

In September 1946, Dr. Noel Harris told the Committee that he proposed to resign the position of Physician-in-Charge. He said that his decision to do so at the end of the year was because he felt that the administration of the hospital, together with a consulting practice and the work of a Staff appointment at the Middlesex Hospital, were too much for one person.

He had joined the Staff in 1935, and had served the hospital continually and without a break during the war for over eleven years. During that time the reputation of Woodside has grown and it has become far more widely known among the medical profession. To a very large extent this has been due to the work of Dr. Harris, and the debt owed to him by the hospital is a large one.

The Governors were glad to think that consequent on the amalgamation with the Middlesex, Dr. Harris's association with Woodside would continue. The details of the amalgamation and the consequent birth of the Psychological Branch of the Middlesex Hospital of which St. Luke's-Woodside is an—if not the—essential part is described elsewhere.

XIII

THE NATIONAL HEALTH SERVICE AND AMALGAMATION WITH THE MIDDLESEX HOSPITAL

EARLY in 1945 the future of St. Luke's and Woodside was again a matter of discussion. The Committee considered that at that time it would be premature to approach the Ministry of Health, because, although a White Paper on a National Health Service had been published by the Coalition Government a General Election was impending, and it was impossible, therefore, to foresee what shape the Health Service would take finally. It was, however, agreed that such a service on a national basis was bound to come, and that future developments should be considered and divided tentatively into priorities. As a result, the Committee agreed that in any case their first objective must be the conversion of Woodside into a 100-bedded hospital in order that it should qualify as a teaching hospital in psychological medicine for students and nurses.

The result of the General Election made it obvious that the new Government would produce a National Health Bill as soon as they could.

In November the Committee received, unofficially, reliable information that the authorities were interested in the co-ordination of effort in the science and practice of Medical Psychology, and that they would welcome some consultation between the big teaching hospitals and those voluntary hospitals and other societies that were concerned with, and interested in, scientific and medical psychology with a view to discovering whether, between them, they could put forward proposals likely to find favour with His Majesty's Government and agreeable to themselves. These authorities felt, apparently, that the importance of psychological medicine should be more generally recognised in other branches of hospital work.

On this, a sub-committee was appointed to go further into the question and in a short time they reported that in their opinion, although St. Luke's might still claim to be a registered

Mental Hospital, it would not be financially possible for it to expand into, at most, more than an incomplete group of small units. Such a group would be uneconomical, and in any case unsuitable and insufficient for teaching purposes. They suggested, therefore, that some association with a larger mental hospital, in order to form a "group" where every type of psychological illness could be studied, should be attempted. Such a "group" might, in their opinion, provide the ideal teaching unit.

They reminded the Committee that St. Luke's was a charity, incorporated by Act of Parliament, and anciently associated with the City of London. That being so, some association with the City of London Mental Hospital (the Stone House at Dartford) would be natural, and might be possible. Such a combination would form an institute large enough to include all forms of mental illness.

It should be noted that the sub-committee, when they presented this report, were not in a position to know what scheme of development would be acceptable to the authorities, or would be practicable, within the limitations of the National Health Service. Their suggestion was what they considered the ideal plan, and they felt that the alternative (namely for each teaching hospital to have its own psychiatric unit) would be extremely expensive and even so an incomplete arrangement, and could not be sufficiently complete to ensure an effective teaching section. Their view at this time was that the institution required should be large enough and complete enough to meet the needs of more than one teaching hospital. The limitations imposed by the proposed regional organisation of the National Health Service, which made it impossible for one such group to serve the needs of teaching hospitals in several regions, were not realised at this point in their discussions.

The main Committee, however, accepted this report in principle, and referred it to the General Court. At a special meeting of the Court the following resolution was passed:

"The General Court have taken note of recent reports of the British Medical Association, the Royal College of Physicians, the Royal Medico-Psychological Association, and other bodies, that the teaching of Psychological Medicine falls short of what is desirable and necessary.

174

"They have considered the steps which might be taken to improve matters, particularly by St. Luke's Hospital, and they are determined to do whatever is possible so far as their resources will allow, but they feel that to create an adequately efficient institute for undergraduate teaching, it would be necessary for it to have many more patients than they could accommodate and maintain. They have, therefore, authorised their Committee to explore the possibilities of some association or co-operation with another hospital, which would further the study of psychological medicine and the teaching of students and nurses with the aim of creating gradually a centre in London for undergraduate education in Psychological Medicine."

Accordingly, an unofficial approach was made to the Visiting Committee of the City of London Mental Hospital to which a copy of the above resolution was sent. But that Committee, after debating the proposal, felt that for the time being nothing could be done in the matter of co-operation between, or amalgamation of, the two hospitals.

Other possibilities had also been considered and explored. St. Luke's was still a member of the Association of Registered Hospitals, and it was thought that possibly as such it might remain independent. At a meeting of this Association at which St. Luke's was represented, it was decided to send a deputation to the Ministry of Health in order to present the case of the registered hospitals. However, the interview between the deputation and the Chairman of the Board of Control did not hold out much promise under the Act of these hospitals retaining their existing semi-independent position and the discussion was felt to be both unsatisfactory and inconclusive.

The opinion of Counsel also was sought in order to ascertain whether St. Luke's Hospital as a Charity incorporated by Act of Parliament, was affected by the Bill. This opinion was that St. Luke's was a separate legal entity which existed apart from the Woodside Hospital or any other assets of the Corporation, but that it could not be shown to be unaffected by the Bill.

The Treasurer of Bethlem was likewise consulted concerning possible co-operation, and it was agreed a scheme should be drawn up by the medical officers of both hospitals, but this also came to nothing largely owing to the fact that the geographical location of the two hospitals was in different London regions.

Finally, the Chairman of the Board of Control was consulted unofficially. He was in full sympathy with the wish of the Governors that St. Luke's should become a teaching, or part of a teaching, hospital, but said that in his view it was not for the Minister, but for the University of the Region, to suggest to the Minister what hospital or group of hospitals should be declared teaching hospitals, and he advised that a representative of the University of London should be consulted. Accordingly, in September 1946 the Physician-in-Charge and the Secretary saw Professor Sir Francis Fraser, whose unofficial opinion was that under the Act the great teaching hospitals would have specialist hospitals linked to them for specialist teaching, and would thus become "teaching groups". His personal advice was that St. Luke's (with Woodside) should link either with the Middlesex or University College Hospital.

The Committee felt that this advice, since it would be acceptable to the authorities and would be in line with the provisions of the Bill, must be accepted by them, though they felt uncertain as to whether the proposed link would conduce to the scientific advance of Medical Psychology or to the teaching of those who intended to specialise in that subject to the same extent as would a large central institution.

They enquired verbally and unofficially both at the Ministry and at the Middlesex Hospital whether the association of St. Luke's and Woodside with the Middlesex would be welcomed by that hospital with which they had been so closely associated in the past. From both there was an encouraging reply, and the Treasurer, therefore, wrote to the Chairman of the Middlesex suggesting a meeting of representatives of both hospitals to discuss the proposal and settle the preliminary steps to be taken.

This meeting took place on the 21st October. The representatives of the Board of the Middlesex expressed their pleasure at, and their full agreement with, the suggested amalgamation, and the Secretary-Superintendent of the Middlesex and the Secretary of St. Luke's were instructed to draft a joint letter about the proposal to the Ministry.

This letter, as finally approved, together with a short note on the history of St. Luke's Hospital, was sent on the 31st October. Briefly, it contained proposals envisaging a complete amalgamation of the two hospitals. It explained that the suggestion for amalgamation originated from the wish of the Governors of St. Luke's that the work they had carried on for so many years before and after a Charter was granted to them, should be extended so as to keep pace with modern developments of psychological medicine in all its branches.

The letter went on to state that if the principle of amalgamation were approved, it was proposed to co-opt some of the Governors of St. Luke's as members of the Board of the Middlesex.

Woodside Hospital would become the psychological department of the Middlesex Hospital, and its funds and property would be incorporated in the funds of the Middlesex and operated by the newly constituted Board. Further it was stated that:

> "The Governors of St. Luke's Hospital desire that these funds should be kept separate to meet expenditure connected with Psychological medicine; the Board of the Middlesex see no objection to this course."

No difficulty regarding medical and nursing staffs was likely to arise as Dr. Noel Harris was already a member of the Honorary Staff of the Middlesex as well as Consulting Physician of Woodside, since September 1946, when he had resigned the appointment of Physician-in-Charge.

Finally it reaffirmed that the respective governing bodies saw no objection in principle or in practice to the amalgamation. Indeed, they believed that many advantages would accrue. They were prepared to proceed with the amalgamation subject to the Minister's approval, or, if there were any legal difficulties, with a close association which could lead to complete amalgamation as soon as the legal difficulties had been overcome.

Nine days later on the 9th November, the Minister replied stating that he had no objection to offer to the proposal.

On the 8th February, 1947, a further joint letter was addressed to the Ministry. In this the progress made with the association between the two hospitals was related, and it was asked whether the Minister was now prepared to designate the two hospitals as one Teaching Hospital, as this would clear away certain legal difficulties. This, however, was not immediately possible, and it was not until the 23rd April, 1948, that a list of all teaching hospitals under the National Health Service was published. The Middlesex Hospital was designated as one of the teaching hospitals and the group of which it was the centre included St. Luke's Foundation and other establishments.

The Bill became law on the 5th July, 1948, when the amalgamation was completed and became fully operative. St. Luke's Hospital, as a separate entity, ceased to exist, and became the St. Luke's-Woodside Branch of the Middlesex Hospital.

Two of the Governors, Sir Hugh Turnbull and Sir Desmond Morton became members of the Middlesex Board.

In their final report for 1947 for the period 1st January to the 4th July, 1948, the General Committee included both their own and that of the Physician-in-Charge, so as to cover the medical as well as the administrative aspects of the period, and to explain the steps taken by the authorities of both hospitals, not so much to bring the activities of St. Luke's Hospital to an end, as to prepare this ancient foundation for a new lease of life, and for a larger opportunity for serving those who need the help of psychological medicine in conjunction with one of the greater teaching hospitals of London.

Following this, Dr. Harris submitted a memorandum on organisation, whereby the St. Luke's Group would become an essential part of the Department of Psychological Medicine of the Middlesex Hospital. This took the form of a letter previously considered and approved by the Governors of St. Luke's, to the Chairman of the Medical Committee of the Middlesex Hospital, who was asked to bring before his Committee Dr. Harris's suggestions for dealing with:

(1) The immediate needs of the Psychological Department of the hospital.
(2) Completion of integration on amalgamation with Woodside.
(3) The creation of a fully equipped psychological unit for the Middlesex Hospital.

After mentioning the existing lack of accommodation for psychological work at the Middlesex, and the general and growing recognition of the importance of psychosomatic medicine

178

and close co-operation between departments, Dr. Harris pointed out that some of the accommodation required could be provided at Woodside where the bomb-damaged wing would shortly be re-built, and where Lea Wood could also be used. But, even so, there was not enough accommodation at Woodside for out-patients. However, a plan for an out-patient block had been prepared by Mr. O. P. Milne, F.R.I.B.A., and it was hoped, when it had been approved by the Middlesex Hospital, eventually to submit it to the Minister.

There was also sufficient space in the grounds of Woodside for an Occupational Therapy and Sports Bungalow, and if Lea Wood were added to or rebuilt, a still larger number of patients could be accommodated.

Finally, Dr. Harris reminded the Medical Committee that on Welders Estate there was room for modern psychological buildings and a base hospital as well.

Dr. Harris asked for the following eventual establishment. (This included the present staff):

> An Honorary Assistant Physician.
> 3 Senior Resident Physicians.
> 1 whole-time Research Worker.
> Up to 6 Assistant Physicians for out-patients.
> 4 Clinical Assistants.
> 2 House Physicians.
> 1 Occupational Therapist.
> Up to 3 Psychiatric Social Workers.
> 1 Educational Psychologist.
> 1 Play-Therapist.

He admitted that while the scheme he had outlined did not provide sufficient material to teach students all that was necessary in psychoses and cases of mental deficiency, where visits to suitable hospitals would still be necessary, it did provide an adequate means for teaching them what is more important, namely, the place of psychology in general medicine, how to deal with ordinary everyday psychological problems, and also how to handle neuroses. The scheme should also enable the Department to go a long way towards qualifying as a training school for nurses wishing to take the R.M.P.A. certificate or Psychiatric Section of the General Nursing Council's examination.

Subsequently, Dr. Hobson, who had recently obtained the Membership of the Royal College of Physicians, was approved as Honorary Assistant Physician in the Department of Psychological Medicine, while Dr. T. T. Bartlett, M.R.C.S., L.R.C.P., and Dr. E. A. Chennell, M.B., B.S., D.P.M., were appointed to the staff of Woodside Hospital, their appointments being confirmed by the Middlesex Hospital.

On the amalgamation, the Secretary of St. Luke's, Brigadier C. N. French, C.M.G., C.B.E., retired and was elected to the new House Committee of Woodside Hospital.

FUTURE SYSTEM OF ADMINISTRATION

Apart from the fact that to become a teaching hospital has always been the wish of the Governors of St. Luke's there are definite advantages in this status, as will be seen from the difference between teaching and non-teaching hospitals in the National Health Scheme.

The Minister of Health, who is responsible to Parliament for the whole service, is advised by a Central Health Service Council and Standing Advisory Committee. For administration of the hospital and consultant and specialist services, the country is divided into regions with Regional Hospital Boards. These appoint Hospital Management Committees to individual hospitals or groups of hospitals.

But in the case of teaching hospitals, the Boards of Governors for each individual hospital or group of hospitals are the Minister's direct agents. They are not appointed by or subordinate to the Regional Boards, but are expected to keep in close touch and collaborate with them. They appoint the House Committee for each unit in their group.

In the case of Woodside, the Board of the Middlesex asked the Governors of St. Luke's to nominate members of the House Committee with the happy result that all members of that Committee are either ex-Governors of St. Luke's or were members of the Woodside staff before affiliation took place, and two of the members are on the Board of the Middlesex.

This House Committee, at their first meeting, invited the late Treasurer of St. Luke's to accept the position of Honorary President, an invitation which he gladly accepted. There is, therefore, every reason to hope and believe that the traditions and spirit of the old hospital will endure.

The endowments of non-teaching hospitals are transferred to the Minister, but the endowments of teaching hospitals are transferred to the Boards of Governors, and consequently the General Fund of St. Luke's has been transferred to the Board of Governors of the Middlesex Hospital. In any case, the amalgamation of the hospitals makes the sanction of the Middlesex Board necessary for all expenditure of St. Luke's-Woodside and Welders. The House Committee recommends but cannot approve, expenditure, except in the case of small sums and urgent matters. As well as annual budgets, bills and wages are approved weekly and monthly before actual payment.

This procedure sounds complicated and calculated to delay progress, and so it is up to a point, but the pleasant relations existing between the respective administrations and staffs, and the consideration and helpfulness shown by all representatives of the larger hospital, have so far ensured the smooth, and, it is hoped, the efficient working of the machine.

It is, therefore, in a hopeful spirit that the story of St. Luke's as an independent institution from 1750 to 1948 is concluded. It is the story of 198 years of voluntary effort by the Governors of an organisation initiated by citizens of the City of London. Originally, they had hoped to treat patients free, but economic conditions and the inexorable and inevitable increase in every kind of expense, together with the rising standard of comfort demanded of all hospitals, disappointed this hope. They were compelled in consequence to ask their patients to contribute something towards their cost on a sliding scale according to their means. Thus they were able to maintain their general fund, and indeed to increase it when the hospital in Old Street was sold. On amalgamation with the Middlesex Hospital, St. Luke's did not join the group empty-handed, but contributed not only a modern and well-equipped hospital, but also a fund that, even by present costly standards, could help to some extent to maintain the St. Luke's-Woodside section of that hospital.

But far more essential than these material assets has been the contribution of this ancient Foundation to the study of mental illness and psychological medicine. The confidence of the original founders that the advantages of their hospital would ensure that "more gentlemen of the Faculty" would make "this branch of Physick their particular care and study", and that the cure of this disease "would hereafter be rendered more certain and expeditious", has indeed been justified.

This is not intended as a claim that St. Luke's has been alone in its work, for many other individuals and institutions in this country and elsewhere have played a notable part in the study of psychological medicine. But it can be claimed, without exaggeration, that in this period of nearly 200 years, St. Luke's has had a not unworthy share both in charity and in medical progress.

APPENDIX I

Presidents

Earl of Cardigan (afterwards Duke of Montagu)	1751-1790
Fifth Duke of Leeds	1790-1799
Sixth Duke of Leeds	1799-1838
Earl of Clarendon	1838-1839
H.R.H. (First) Duke of Cambridge	1839-1850
Lord Overstone	1851-1874
S. J. Whitbread, Esq., F.R.S.	1875-1879
H.R.H. (Second) Duke of Cambridge	1880-1904
Tenth Duke of Leeds	1906-1927
Major-General The Earl of Athlone (President, St. Luke's and Woodside Hospitals)	1931-1948

Treasurers

William Davy, Esq.	1751-1773
William Prowting, Esq.	1773-1794
David Powell, Esq.	1794-1810
John Clark Powell, Esq.	1810-1843
Henry Francis Shaw Lefevre, Esq.	1843-1879
General Sir Henry de Bathe	1879-1887
Arthur Powell, Esq.	1887-1890
Edward W. Nix, Esq.	1890-1901
Arthur Crofts Powell, Esq.	1901-1925
The Rt. Hon. Lord Blanesburgh	1925-1946
Brigadier-General Sir George Cockerill	1946-1948

Consulting and Visiting Physicians

William Battie, M.D.	1750-1764
Thomas Brooke, M.D.	1764-1781
Samuel Foart Simmons, F.R.S., M.D.	1781-1811
Alexander Robert Sutherland, M.D.	1811-1841
John Warburton, M.D.	1829-1842
Alexander John Sutherland, M.D.	1841-1859
Francis Richard Philp, M.D.	1842-1854
Henry Monro, M.B.	1855-1891

Medical Superintendents

Mr. Henry Stephens, M.R.C.S.	1856-1860
Mr. Ebenezer Toller, M.R.C.S.	1860-1863
Mr. Octavius Jepson, M.R.C.S.	1863-1864
Mr. James Ellis, M.R.C.S.	1864-1868
Mr. J. Thompson Dickson, M.R.C.S.	1869-1870
Mr. Reginald Eager, M.R.C.S., M.A., M.B.	1870-1876
Mr. George Mickley, M.A., M.B.	1876-1898
Mr. William Rawes, F.R.C.S.	1899-1916

Surgeons

Mr. John Sheron	1751-1755
Mr. John James	1755-1866
Mr. John Waring	1766-1780
Mr. George Chandler	1780-1783
Mr. Henry Cline	1783-1785
Mr. George Vaux	1785-1820
Mr. John Dunston, F.R.C.S.	1830-1832
Mr. James Luke, F.R.C.S.	1832-1866
Mr. Charles Hewitt Moore, F.R.C.S.	1866-1870
Mr. Alfred Willett, F.R.C.S.	1870-1906

Apothecaries

Mr. William Bagster	1766-1772
Mr. John Harris	1772
Mr. John Meadows	1772-1809
Mr. George D'Aranda	1814-1817
Mr. John Thomas	1817-1828
Mr. Joseph Stephen Barnes	1828-1842
Mr. Henry Lambert	1842-1848
Mr. Joseph Nash	1848-1850
Mr. John Thomas Arlidge	1850-1852
Mr. Henry Stevens, M.R.C.S.	1853-1856

Physicians-in-Charge, Woodside Hospital

Dr. R. W. Gilmour, M.B., M.R.C.P.	1930-1935
Dr. Noel Harris, F.R.C.P.	1935-1948

Secretaries

Thomas Webster, Esq.	1750-1787
John Webster, Esq.	1787-1826

Thomas Webster, Esq.	1826-1849
George Mence, Esq.	1849-1858
Thomas J. A. Jenkins, Esq.	1858-1859
J. F. Whisken, Esq.	1859-1869
Rev. T. H. Cole (Secretary-Chaplain)	1869-1871
George Seymour, Esq.	1871-1875
H. C. Crespin, Esq.	1875-1882
H. C. Crespin, Esq. (Secretary-Steward)	1882-1884
P. de Bathe, Esq.	1884-1896
W. H. Baird, Esq. (Secretary-Steward)	1896-1932
Alfred B. Nutter, Esq., O.B.E.	1932-1943
Brigadier C. N. French, C.M.G., C.B.E.	1943-1948
Mrs. P. C. Thompson (Secretary, Woodside Hospital)	1943-1948

Keepers, Masters and Matrons

Joseph and Mary Mansfield	1751-1782
James and Elizabeth Pearson	1782
Thomas and Mary Dunston	1782-1816
Thomas Dunston (Superintendent)	1816-1830
James and Mary Tow	1816-1830
William and Clementina Stinton	1830-1849
Thomas Collier Walker ⎰ Charlotte Eliza Walker ⎱	1849-1882

Stewards

H. C. Crespin, Esq.	1882-1884
Thomas Glover, Esq.	1884-1890
W. H. Baird, Esq.	1890-1932

Matrons

Miss C. A. Burrows	1882-1883
Miss B. E. Sterne	1883-1904
Miss M. Kirk	1904-1908
Miss P. Head	1908-1914
Miss L. A. Hunt	1914-1937
Miss I. E. Tebbutt	1937-1943
Miss M. W. Squires	1943-1944
Miss C. Nuthall	1944-1947

Sister-in-Charge

Miss S. E. Clark	1947-1948

G   185

APPENDIX II

I. *Qualification of Governor. Exception to Physicians, etc.*

That every person, except as hereinafter accepted, paying (in his own right) to the Treasurer for the time being, for the use of this Hospital, the entire sum of Twenty Guineas or upwards, or paying five Guineas at least, and signing an Agreement (in a Book to be kept for that purpose) to pay five Guineas yearly for the four next succeeding years, shall be admitted a Governor of this Hospital, and receive by the hands of the Secretary, a Staff, a printed copy of the Rules and Orders; save and except all previous acting as Physician, Surgeon, Apothecary or Secretary to this Hospital (other than the six Apothecaries declared Governors at the general Meeting, held the 29th day of June, 1750) during the time they shall respectively Act in those capacities.

II. *General Courts when to be held*

That for the transacting the Business of this Hospital, a General Court shall be held twice in every Year, viz., on the second Wednesday in the months of February and August, and at such other times as hereinafter mentioned, and that every General Court shall consist of thirty Governors at least.

III. *Officers and General Committee when to be elected. Physicians, etc., of other Hospitals not eligible*

That at the General Court to be held annually on the second Wednesday in the month of February, one President, four Vice-Presidents, a Treasurer, a General Committee, Physician, Surgeon, Apothecary and Secretary, shall be elected for the year ensuing. And that no person acting as Physician, Surgeon or Apothecary to any other Hospital or Infirmary, shall be eligible to be Physician, Surgeon or Apothecary to this Hospital.

IV. *Who to preside at Courts and Committees*

That in all General Courts and Committees, the President (or in his absence) one of the Vice-Presidents, or in case no

186

Vice-President shall be present, the Treasurer shall preside. But in case of the absence of the President, Vice-Presidents and Treasurer, or of their quitting the chair before the Business of such Court or Committee shall be finished, a President or Chairman shall be elected for that time, out of the Governors then present.

V. *What questions shall be put*

That the person presiding at such respective Meetings, shall put all such Questions, and no other, as shall be moved and seconded.

VI. *How to be determined*

That all questions shall be determined by the Majority of Governors present, and holding up hands, or by a Division, or by a Ballot, in case the same shall be required by seven or more Governors before a Division is begun, such Ballot to be proceeded on immediately.

VII. *President to have a casting vote*

That in all cases of an equality of votes, the Person providing for the time being shall have a double or casting Vote.

VIII. *Person speaking to stand up*

That in all Debates the person speaking shall stand up, and address himself to the Chair, and no person shall speak more than twice on the same Question without leave.

IX. *When two speak, President to direct*

That when two or more offer to speak at the same time, the President or Chairman shall direct which of them is to proceed.

X. *Auditors when to be chose*

That at the General Court to be held annually on the second Wednesday in the Month of August, a special Committee of seven, Governors (who are not of the general Committee) shall be appointed to audit and examine the several Accounts relating to this Hospital, with their Vouchers, which Committee are to report their opinion of such Accounts to the General Court, to be held on the second Wednesday in February following. At which General Court the said Accounts, signed by three of the Auditors at least, made up to the first day of January then last past, shall be laid before the Governors by the Treasurer for their Approbation.

XI. *Special General Court. How to be called*

That the President have power to order special General Courts to be summoned as often as he thinks necessary, and in the case of the Death, or absence, or Omission to order a General Court within the time hereafter limited, one of the Vice-Presidents at the request of the General Committee (signified by letter from the Secretary containing the reasons for the same) or of any twelve Governors (signified by Writing under their Hands containing their reasons for the same) shall order a Special General Court to be summoned and held within fourteen days next after such Request; at which Court the said Letter or Visiting shall be publickly read.

XII. *In case of vacancy in office of Treasurer, etc.*

That upon every vacancy in the Office of Treasurer, Physician, Surgeon, Apothecary or Secretary, the Committee shall signify the same by Writing to the President or in case of his Death or Absence, to one of the Vice-Presidents, who shall order a General Court to be summoned to meet within fourteen days next after such Notice, to declare such vacancy, and appoint a time for an Election to fill up the same, which shall be between the sixth and fourteenth days next after such Declaration. And that no person be entitled to vote at any such Election at a General Court, unless he shall have paid his Subscription Money, on, or before the day, in which a Vacancy shall be declared.

XIII. *What notice to be given of General Courts*

That three days Notice at least of every General Court shall be given to all Governors residing within the Bills of Mortality, and Notice of such General Court shall be given in one or more of the publick Newspapers, which Notice shall express the Business for which such Court is called, and no other Business shall be then proceeded on, in case the same shall be objected to by twelve Governors then present.

XIV. *General Committee. Who to consist of. Five to do business*

That the General Committee shall consist of the President, Vice-President, and Treasurer for the time being, and of the five Governors named as Lessees in the Lease of the Ground on which this Hospital is built, and of all Persons who shall have paid for the use of this Hospital the sum of £100 or upwards, who shall be standing Members thereof, and of such twenty-four other Governors residing within the Bills of Mortality, as shall be annually elected for that purpose, at the General Court to be held on the second Wednesday in February, of which Committee five at least shall be necessary to do Business.

XV. *General Committee, when to meet. Their power and Business*

That the General Committee do meet one stated day in every Month, or oftner (sic) if they shall see convenient, and at such other times as the Treasurer, or any sub-Committee for the time being shall appoint. And that they have power to hire, govern and discharge the Domestick Servants of this Hospital, keep the Buildings properly repaired and purchase provisions, Furniture, and other necessaries for the same. To admit and discharge patients according to the Rules hereafter mentioned. To see that the several Books relating to the Hospital be regularly kept. That all Debts, Legacies, annual Subscriptions, and other revenues of this Hospital be received as the same shall respectively become due. That all Moneys in the Hands of the Treasurer, above what is necessary in the opinion of the said Committee, for defraying the current expenses of the Hospital, be from time to time placed out in transferable Government Securities, and no other, in the Names of the Treasurer for the time being, and two of the Vice-Presidents, or of two such other Governors as the General Court shall appoint for that purpose. And that all just demands upon this Hospital be regularly discharged, at least once in six months. And in general, the said Committee are to make such Rules for the Management and Economy of the Hospital as they shall find necessary, and to cause them to be inserted in Books to be kept for that purpose; and to propose for the Consideration of the General Courts, all such matters as shall appear to them conducive to the good of this Charity.

XVI. *To keep Minutes*

That the said Committee do keep Minutes of all their proceedings.

XVII. *To appoint sub-Committees*

That for the more easy dispatch of Business, the said Committee have power to appoint sub-Committees, one of which shall be called the House Committee, and that such sub-Committees have power from time to time to summon the General Committee as they shall think proper.

XVIII. *Purchase to be by contract. Not with any member of the Committee*

That all purchases of provisions and other Materials shall be made as often as possible by contract. But no contract shall be made in or by which any Member of the Committee shall be directly or indirectly interested or concerned.

XIX. *Treasurer to pay Bills and Drafts*

That the Treasurer for the time being do pay all Bills and Drafts, signed by three Members of the General Committee, and none other which shall exceed the sum of forty shillings.

XX. *His power and Business*

That the Treasurer be empowered to receive all Benefactions, annual Subscriptions, Debts, Legacies, and other Revenues of this Hospital, and to give discharges for the same respectively. That he shall cause Books to be kept with such Bankers as shall be approved by the General Committee, for taking in all such Sums as well disposed persons may be inclined to contribute to this Charity. That he do annually, between the 31st December and 1st of February, lay a general state of his accounts with their Vouchers before the Auditors for their Examination. That he do report at every Monthly Meeting of the said Committee, all such new sums as he shall have received, that the same may be entered into the several books to be kept for that purpose. That all Securities upon the Admission of Patients into this Hospital, or for the Fidelity and good Behaviour of any Officer or Servant thereof, and all contracts with Tradesmen or others, shall be taken and made in the name of the Treasurer for the time being, and that he be empowered to summon a General Committee as often as he shall think proper.

XXI. *Secretary, his Business*

That the Secretary shall summon General Courts and Committees, and take Minutes of the proceedings thereof and enter the same in the Proper Books (together with the names of the Governors then present) before the next Meeting of such Court of Committee, when he shall read the same, previous to any other Business, and when confirmed, the same shall be signed by the President or Chairman for the time being.

XXII. *To keep Books, etc.*

That the Secretary keep Books, write letters, and do such other Business relating to this Hospital as shall be ordered or directed by the General Courts and Committees.

XXIII

That no Governor or other person (unless desired) be present at any matter relating to himself is under consideration.

XXIV. *Complaints, how to be made*

That any Officer or Servant having cause of complaint, shall signify the same in Writing either to the General or House Committee.

XXV

That the Committee have power to relieve any patient, at his or her Discharge, with any sum not exceeding twenty shillings.

XXVI. *Physician, when to attend*

That the Physician do attend this Hospital every weekly Committee Day, and one other day in the Week, at two days distance at least, and as often otherwise as there shall be Occasion.

XXVII. *Surgeon, when to attend*

That the Surgeon do attend the Hospital every Weekly Committee day, and as often otherwise as there shall be occasion.

XXVIII. *Apothecary, when to attend*

That the present six Apothecaries do attend the Hospital by Rotation monthly, and that the Apothecary in Rotation do attend every weekly Committee Day, and two other days in every week, and as often at other times as there shall be occasion.

XXIX. *No Physician, etc., to officiate, for established Physician, etc., unless*

That no Physician, Surgeon or Apothecary shall officiate in the place of the established Physician, Surgeon or Apothecary, without first obtaining the consent of the General or House Committee.

XXX. *Officer or Servant taking any fee, to be discharged. Except Secretary*

That every officer or Servant who shall take any Fee, Gratuity or Reward, directly or indirectly, from any Tradesman or other person dealing with this Hospital, Patient or Friend of any patient in respect of any services done or to be done, shall forthwith be discharged, and rendered incapable of being received again into the service of this Hospital. Except that it shall be lawful for the Secretary of this Hospital, upon his waiting on every Governor with a Staff and a printed copy of the Rules and Orders of this Hospital, to accept of a Fee not exceeding one Guinea.

XXXI. *Rules relating to Officers, Servants, where to be kept*

That Rules and Orders which relate to the conduct of the Officers of this Hospital, be fairly entered in a Book to be kept for that purpose in some convenient place, where the Governors of this Hospital may have the perusal of the same, and that such rules as relate to the Servants be hung up in some conspicuous place in the Hospital.

XXXII. *Petition to be registered*

That every Petition (having the necessary Certificates annexed) for the Admission of a Patient, shall be signed by a Governor of this Hospital, and registered by the Secretary immediately on the delivery of it to him, together with the exact time of such Delivery.

XXXIII. *Patients, when to be taken in*

That the Patients shall be taken into this Hospital according to the order of time in which their petitions have been delivered in to the Secretary, without Favour or Partiality, and shall be admitted without any Expense, except only that such of them who are parish Poor shall provide their own Bedding which they are at liberty to take away at their Discharge.

XXXIV. *Bond on every Admission of Patients*

That on the admission of every Patient, two responsible Housekeepers residing within the Bills of Mortality (whose Names with their places of Abode, shall have been left in Writing with the Secretary four days before such admission and who shall be approved of by the Committee) shall enter into a Bond to the Treasurer for the time being, in the penalty of £100 to take away such patient within seven days after Notice given to them for that purpose by the Committee or their Secretary. But no Governor of this Hospital shall be Security for any Patient.

XXXV

That the Patients in this Hospital be not exposed to publick view.

XXXVI. *Complaints against Officers and Servants to be entered in a Book*

That a Book (entitled the Visitors' Book) shall be kept in some convenient publick place of the Hospital, for the Governors to enter complaints of any neglect or misconduct in the Officers or Servants thereof, which Complaints shall be subscribed with the Name of the Person making the same, to the Intent it may be taken into Consideration and regarded by the Committee that a Charity Box with two different Locks be provided and fixed up in some convenient and publick place in the Hospital; That one of the Keys be constantly kept by the Treasurer, and the other by some Member of the Committee, and that the Money be not taken out, but in the presence or by Order of the Committee.

XXXVIII. *No Money to be expended in Entertainment*

That no Moneys received for the use of this Charity, be expended in entertaining the General Court or Committee at any of the Meetings.

XXXIX. *Buildings to be plain and substantial*

That the Building and Furniture of this Hospital be plain and substantial, and without ornament, and that no Building be erected without an order for that purpose from the General Court.

XL. *Rules and Orders not to be repealed unless, etc.*

That none of these Rules and Orders be repealed, but by a General Court of Governors, in which fifty at least shall be consenting thereto. Or the Majority of that and the next succeeding General Court.

APPENDIX III

1. That no person shall knowingly be received as a Patient into this Hospital who is not in point of Circumstances a proper Object of this Charity, that is, Poor and Mad.
2. Or who hath been a Lunatick more than twelve Calendar Months.
3. Or who hath been discharged uncured from any other Hospital for the Reception of Lunaticks.
4. Or who is troubled with Epileptick or Convulsive Fits.
5. Or who is deemed an Idiot.
6. Or who is infected with the Venereal Disease.
7. Nor any Woman with child.

And every such person who, through Mistake or Misinformation, shall be received into this Hospital, shall be discharged immediately on a Discovery of any of the above Disqualifications.

Therefore, if the Patient is not disqualified by any of the above Rules, upon applying to Mr. Thomas Webster the Secretary, at his House in Queen Street, Cheapside, or at the Hospital, the Forms of two printed Certificates, together with a petition, may be had; the first of which Certificates (after it is filled up) must be signed by the Minister and Church Warden, or Overseer of the poor of the parish, or place, where such patient resided; and the other by some Physician, Surgeon, or Apothecary, who hath visited such patient; after which the person or persons who saw them sign must go before one of His Majestie's Justices of the Peace, or some other person authorised to take Affidavits, and make Oath (or in case of Quakers, an Affirmation) in the manner as is printed at the Bottom of the said Certificates.

When the certificates have been thus signed, and Oath (or Affirmation) made thereof as aforesaid, the next step is to fill up the Petition, and annex the certificate thereto, and then to apply to a Governor to sign the same, which being done, both the Petition and Certificates must be left with the Secretary, and the Petitioner must not fail to attend at the Hospital the next Friday Morning at 10 o'clock, when the same will be laid before the Committee, and if approved, an Order will be made for the Patient to be brought for examination, in his turn, as soon as a Vacancy happens; four Days, at least, before which there must be left in Writing with the Secretary, the Names, Business and places of abode of two substantial House-keepers residing within the Bills of Mortality, who must be present precisely at 11 o'clock in the Morning, when the patient is to be admitted, to enter into a Bond of £100 to take the patient away when discharged by the Committee.

N.B. No Governor of the Hospital can be Security for any Patient.

APPENDIX IV

To the President, Vice-Presidents, Treasurer and Governors of St. Luke's Hospital for Lunaticks

Certificate to be signed by the Minister and 2 Church-wardens of the Parish.

We whose Names are hereunto sub-scribed the Minister of   of the parish of   in the County of   do certify to the best of our Knowledge and Belief that   now residing in this Parish is a Lunatick, and in point of Circum-stances a proper Object of your Charity. That   became so dis-ordered about the   day of   last. That   hath not been discharged uncured from any other Hospital for the Reception of Lunaticks. That   is not troubled with Epileptick or Convulsive Fits, or deemed an Idiot. And that   hath received Alms from   Parish.

Here insert whether the patient has or has not received alms.

Witness our Hands the   day of 175 .

Certificate to be signed by a Physician, Surgeon or Apothecary.

I, the underwritten   of the parish of   in the county of   do certify that   of the parish of   in the County of   if a Lunatick. And in point of Circum-stances a proper Object of Charity. That   is not troubled with Epileptick or Convulsive Fits, or deemed an Idiot. Witness my Hand the day of   175 .

197

Here insert the Names of the persons who signed both the Certificates as above.

maketh Oath that he did see the said severally sign their Names to the above Certificates.

Sworn the Day of 175 before

N.B. It is desired that such Physician, Apothecary or Surgeon do by Letter directed to the Physicians of this Hospital, to be delivered at the Weekly Committee, send a state of such Patients case, and an Account of the Methods (if any) need to obtain a cure.

TO THE PRESIDENT, VICE-PRESIDENTS, TREASURER AND GOVERNORS OF ST. LUKE'S HOSPITAL FOR LUNATICKS, LONDON

Form of Petition.

The Humble petition of
on the behalf of
of the Parish of
In the County of

SHEWETH,

That in regard the said is a Lunatick, and a proper Object of your Charity, as appears by the annexed Certificates.

Your Petitioner humbly prays that the said may be admitted as a patient into your Hospital in order to h cure, And you Petitioner shall ever pray, etc.

Here the Petitioner is to sign his Name.

I desire the said Lunatick may be admitted a patient into St. Luke's Hospital for Lunaticks, if a fit object.

APPENDIX V

For the Physician

That the Physician do attend this Hospital every weekly
Committee day and one other day in the Week at two days'
distance at least, and as often otherwise as there shall be
occasion.

For the Surgeon

That the Surgeon do attend the Hospital every Weekly
Committee Day and as often otherwise as there shall be
occasion.

For the Apothecary

That the present six Apothecaries do attend the Hospital
by Rotation Monthly and that the Apothecary in rotation do
attend every Weekly Committee day and two other days in
every Week and as often at other times as there shall be
Occasion.

That no Physician, Surgeon or Apothecary shall officiate
in the place of the established Physician, Surgeon or Apothecary
without first obtaining the consent of the General or House
Committee.

For the Man and Woman Keepers

1. That it shall be the Business of the Man keeper to weigh
in all the respective provisions ordered for daily Diet of the
house and keep an exact Account thereof. And that it be the
joint Business of the Man and Woman Keepers to see the same
daily distributed to the patients at such times and in such
proportions as shall be ordered.

2. That he takes care that the house be locked up at Nine
of the Clock in the Evening and not opened before seven in
the Morning from Michaelmas to Ladyday, and locked at ten
in the Evening and not opened till six in the Morning from
Ladyday to Michaelmas.

3. That he have the care of the Household furniture, and be
ready to account for it according to the Inventory signed by
him. That he see that the Men Servants perform their Duty

and that he do not permit any strong Beer, Spirituous Liquors, Tea or provisions of any kind to be brought into the House to the patients from their friends or any person whatever.

4. That she have the care of the Household Linen, and overlook the Washing, and see that the Maid Servants perform their Duty.

For the Messenger or Porter

1. That he attend the Door to prevent any of the patients going out, and inform one of the Keepers when any stranger comes in. And that he do not take upon himself to give Answers without calling a Superior Servant. .

2. That when he shall be employed upon the Business of the House without Doors he give Notice to one of the Keepers that somebody be ordered to take Charge of the Door till his Return.

3. That he deliver Summonses to the Governors when ordered, and attend and obey all Orders of the Committees Treasurer.

4. That when he is not employed on the above Attendances he do all the labouring Business of the house, as he shall be ordered from time to time by the Keepers.

For the Maid Servants

That they clean the House every day before ten of the Clock, dress the Victuals, Wash and assist in the Care of the Patients.

That all the Inferior Servants are diligent in complying with the Orders of the Keepers and their other Superiors, and behave themselves properly to the Patients, and with civility and respect to all Strangers. That neither the Porter or Maid Servants do presume to go out of the Hospital on any Account whatsoever without leave of the Keeper, and that both the Keepers be not absent at the same time on any pretence whatsoever.

That every Officer or Servant who shall take any Fee, Gratuity or Reward directly or indirectly from any Tradesman dealing with the Hospital, Patient or Friend of any patient, or from any other person in respect of any Services done or to be done shall forthwith be discharged, and rendered incapable of being received again into the Service of this Hospital.

That any Officer or Servant having cause of complaint shall signify the same in Writing either to the General or House Committee.

INDEX

Abolition of restraint, 125

Accessibility, importance of, for St. Luke's, 70

Accommodation for staff, 103, 130, 132

Act for the Care and Treatment of Lunatics, 1845, 57

Act of Incorporation, 1838, 54, 103

Additional beds at Woodside, 168

Administration, 58, 75, 78, 162, 180, 182

Admissions limited, 171

"Afflicted of God", 1

Agreement regarding division of sale price, 115

Agreement with the Middlesex Hospital, 1923, 144, 145

Airing Courts and Grounds, 56, 69, 80, 105, 122

Air-raids, 117, 161-2, 171

Alcoholism, 133, 145, 158

Allowance of bread, 19, 25

Almoner, House Committee acts as, 95

Amalgamation with the Middlesex Hospital under the National Health Act, 176, approved, 177, completed, 178

Amusement and occupation, 44, 55, 73, 80, 84, 85, 88, 120, 123

Annual Report, physicians', 43, 57, 91, 120

Anti-spasmodics, 38, 122

Anxiety, 157, 158, 163, 164

Apothecaries, six to supply free drugs, 6, 14

Apothecaries, List of, Appendix I

Apothecary, 46, 87, 118, 127

Appeals for funds, 5, 6, 102

Arbitrator, independent on sale of Old Street site suggested, 114

Architect and Contractors of 2nd St. Lukes' made Governors, 32

Army Nurses, 138

Army Physical Training Corps, 163

Ashley, Lord, see Shaftesbury

Assets of the Hospital, 34

Assistant to Matron, 26, 118

Assistant to Medical Superintendent, 95, 103

Associated rooms, patients chained at night, 39, 46, 55

Association of registered mental hospitals, 175

Association of a mental with a general hospital, 143

Association of Woodside with a larger mental hospital, 173-4

Asylum or hospital, distinction, 72, 81

Asylums, County, 41

Athlone, Major General, the Earl of, 154, 168

Attendants, 25, 33, 45, 75, 82, 96, 118, et seq.

Attendants or nurses, head for each ward, 130

Attendant male, 128, 130, 131

Attributability, owing to war, 163

Authority, divided within the Hospital, 86, 87, 128, 131

Backgammon, 122

Bacon, price of, 49

Bagatelle Tables, 45, 122

Bagley, Matthew, 10

Baird, Mr. W. H., 155, 167

Balls, fortnightly, 125

Bank of England, 38, 52, 106, 116

Banner, Mr. Peter Banner, carpenter, 29, 32

Bartlett, Dr. T., 166, 180

Basement, 37, 73, 75, 80

Baths, 13, 37, 39, 44, 81, 84, 105, 120

Bath, cold plunge, 13, 37, 39, 81, 121

Batson's Coffee House in Cornhill, 28

Battie, Dr. William, 12, 17, 18, 23, 121 122

Beaconsfield, 137, 140

Beating and whipping of insane persons, 1

Bedding, 37, 51, 79

Beef and mutton, price of, 19, 25, 34

Beer, small, 19, 35

Beer, issue to the staff discontinued, 1903, 132

Belgium, colony estate for the insane, 73

Belladonna, 123

Belt and locked gloves, 129

Bethlem Hospital, 2, 3, 4, 5, 14, 39, 51, 52, 57, 75, 175

Bicycle rides, 103

Billiard table, 84, 103

Bills and receipts for the 1st St. Luke's, 12

Birds in cages, 84

Bishopsgate, site of Old Bethlem, 3

H   201

H*   203